Recommended Teaching & Learning Pathway

for using **Social Thinking Thinksheets**

for Tweens and Teens

Social Thinking Thinksheets for Tweens and Teens should be used with products designed to teach individuals ages 10-18

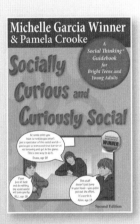

Ages 9-13   Ages 10-18   Ages 12-18   Ages 13-Adult

Thinksheets for Teens and Tweens provides over 160 mini-lessons to expand on the social emotional teachings provided in the above products.

Find these and other books and teaching materials at
www.SocialThinking.com

Contents

Chapter 3: Problem Solving

Chapter 4: Lessons on Emotions

Chapter 5: Different Perspectives

Chapter 6: Being Bossy and Jerky

Chapter 7: Lessons on Friendship

Chapter 8: The Social Fake and Other Tricks

Chapter 9: Participating in Groups

Bibliography

Acknowledgements
and the Journey of Creating This Product

A s I worked with students who had solid language learning skills yet struggled within the social arena, I found it helpful to teach Social Thinking concepts cognitively and in a manner that encouraged students to personally relate to the lessons. The idea of Social Thinking thinksheets arose out of this teaching goal. They also allow us to more easily share the concepts we explore in Social Thinking groups with parents and other professionals. These thinksheets are powerful tools for teaching abstract social concepts.

After starting my own clinic in San Jose, California, I encouraged my clinic therapists to also create Social Thinking thinksheets. The therapists who worked with me from 1999 to 2006 helped develop some of the teaching ideas presented in this book. Many thanks go to these talented colleagues, including Randi Dodge, Reesa Feldsher, Stephanie Madrigal, Amy Miller, Sue Day, Kristi Iwami, Pamela Crooke, and Jamie Rivetts.

Many thanks also go to Gretchen Schmidt Mertes for inspiring me to develop this book, which became our second book of published thinksheets. She dragged binders filled with thinksheets to her home in the Seattle, Washington, area to select ideas to be considered for this book. After receiving Gretchen's ideas, I decided to dedicate this book specifically to helping our older kids, tweens and teens, learn these increasingly abstract concepts.

As I read through the initial selection of Social Thinking thinksheets, I also realized that our Social Thinking teaching ideas continue to evolve. In 2010, I took my computer to a rented 16th century apartment in Tuscany, Italy, rewrote many of the thinksheets, and added extra lessons based on our more current teachings, all the while taking breaks to walk the cobblestone streets into town to eat gelato. Everyone needs a brain break, even the primary author of this book! I hope you enjoy these resources that have traveled around the world. My goal is to support your teaching of social concepts, social expectations, and social ideas in a way that allows you to tailor the materials, explain them, and elaborate upon them so they are meaningful and relevant for the students or children with whom you work.

Why the Shift from Worksheets to Thinksheets?

For decades, the education community has used the term "worksheets" to describe supplemental teaching materials designed to help students practice a specific concept or lesson. While we also used that term, here at Social Thinking it had a slightly different meaning. For us, worksheets:

- Provided our students time to process and respond more thoughtfully to social learning concepts throughout the entire Social Thinking curriculum;
- Supported Social Thinking's teaching paradigm that our students need to *think* socially before they can problem solve how to adapt their social behaviors (social skills);
- Gave quieter students opportunities to get their voices heard: using thinksheets provides a clearly defined time to share their thoughts and feelings about different concepts with others in the group;
- Were designed to be "mini-lesson plans" for parents and professionals about the concepts being shared, a way to teach many of the Social Thinking ideas explained in our other books;
- Were an effective teaching tool for priming social concepts and helping students connect these ideas to their own experiences.

We didn't think much about the term until one day in the not-so-distant past we had an "a-ha!" moment and realized that not everyone thought about worksheets in the same way. Maybe we needed a different term to describe the material to our community so everyone grasped what they were about at their most basic level (especially for our more literal-minded students with social challenges for whom "worksheets" means "work").

That's the story of how Thinksheets came about, and the reason for the title change in this book—a mini-lesson of its own, of sorts. We're now actively using that term as part of the Social Thinking teaching framework. It echoes that we are first teaching students the thinking part of our social interactions to help them better understand the related social skills they are expected to produce.

PLEASE NOTE: *Only the title has changed; the individual lessons between the covers are the same as in the original* Social Thinking Worksheets for Tweens and Teens *book. It's the same great material, now framed in the way the lessons were intended to be.*

Introduction: Using the Thinksheets

In this book, you'll find thinksheets to help students explore concepts such as learning about the perspectives of others, social problem solving, emotion regulation, and more.

Our thinksheet books are designed to help parents, educators, and therapists build upon the concepts explained in more depth in other materials that are part of the Social Thinking teaching framework. Think of our thinksheet books as companion teaching tools. (See the end of this introduction for information about some of our core books and materials that provide a deeper discussion of the foundational concepts upon which these thinksheets are based.)

The idea of using thinksheets came about when we realized our students with social learning challenges needed direct instruction. Seeing good social skills modeled by others as a means to learn better social behavior just wasn't enough. We need to teach them *explicitly* what most of us do *intuitively* and help them understand that they learn social information in the same way that students learn subjects such as math and science—by studying the topics.

That means as we try to help our students become better social thinkers and social problem solvers, we need to break down abstract social concepts (such as keeping a conversation going, or taking another person's perspective) into small, concrete steps. This helps our students understand not only what skills to use and when but *why* the skills should be used. It's this "why" piece of our teaching that brings about longer-term benefits and helps students internalize their social learning. Social Thinking is all about helping our students learn to *think* about the social situation they're in, look around for social clues and cues, and then make a smart guess based on those clues alongside the perspectives of others to figure out what is expected behavior in the situation.

Thinksheets provide this structured systematic approach to teaching social concepts and related social skills. They are mini-lessons for teaching in a concrete, manageable way. They give you the means to introduce and explore a social concept with your students before they are expected to use it in real-life situations. In doing so, they are better able to observe others in their school, home, or community. Building self-awareness is a big part of social learning.

At our Social Thinking clinic in San Jose, we generally work through the lesson presented in a thinksheet and then facilitate play activities or discussions designed to further explore the concepts being taught. Typically at the end of a session, we invite parents in for a recap of what was taught that day. At that time, we give parents copies of the thinksheets to help them promote their child's understanding of the concepts at home and in the community. We always encourage parents to share the thinksheets with teachers and other professionals involved with their children and enlist their support, when possible, to further reinforce the concepts. I would encourage you to use and share these mini-lessons in a similar manner.

What age range of students is this book designed for?

This book is designed to be used with students with strong language skills, who have normal to above-normal academic learning skills, and who are roughly 10–14 years old.

Material in this book may be used with older students who are less mature or who learn this type of information more slowly.

Who should use the materials in this book?

Any adult caregiver, parent, educator, counselor, speech language pathologist, social worker, occupational therapist, or school principal will benefit from learning about Social Thinking and related skills. In this book, the word "teacher" is used to describe anyone in the treatment community who helps students learn about the social world. The term "parent" is also broadly used to represent anyone in the family, or even a close family friend, who is trying to teach social lessons more explicitly.

A person's social thinking and related social skills are noticed and responded to by everyone, peers and adults alike. Therefore, all materials that make up the Social Thinking teaching framework, including these thinksheets, can be used by anyone who serves as a mentor to students with social learning challenges.

We have also noticed that many neurotypical students can benefit from learning more about their social thinking and social skills, and that even our bright and socially adept students find it interesting to study how the social mind works. This not only aids them in their own lives but also helps them better understand the thoughts, perspectives, and behaviors of characters in novels or people who have shaped our history. While these lessons are readily accepted by most students, our students with social learning challenges will need to study them on a more intensive learning schedule.

We think it's a good idea that students with social learning challenges also receive instruction on Social Thinking outside the mainstream classroom, such as in social skills or social thinking/social learning groups. These groups can be run by a range of professionals, such as speech language pathologists, counselors, occupational therapists, special educators, or gifted paraprofessionals. These lessons also need to be strongly reinforced in the home environment.

. . . .

How do thinksheets help teach Social Thinking and related social skills?

The use of Social Thinking thinksheets is not intended to be the start or the end of the process for parents and teachers. They should be used in the middle of the teaching process to complement information being taught about Social Thinking.

We also want to impress upon teachers and parents that unlike traditional educational worksheets, the thinksheets inside this book were never designed to be copied and distributed to students to work on in isolation, unassociated with teacher-encouraged discussions about these concepts. They were developed as a strategy or lesson guide for you, the professional or parent, to steer your exploration of many different social concepts with your students. Think of them not as stand-alone teaching materials but as adaptable ways to reinforce the social concepts you're working on with students.

Finally, thinksheets were designed to steer you toward more effective teaching:

- There is a tendency to teach social concepts incidentally, while in the process expecting students to use proper social skills. Through the use of thinksheets, we instill the idea that our students can study the development of social learning and social skills in much the same way they learn any other concept, through written materials each student can process and respond to.

- The thinksheets encourage full group participation. Some of the students we worked with were hyper-verbal (talked too much) and others were hypo-verbal (talked too little), yet all were capable verbal communicators. The dilemma became how to teach students who were hypo-verbal, given that the hyper-verbal students were always talking. The use of thinksheets provided a way to focus the attention of all students on particular social concepts. I could then call on specific students to encourage them to think and contribute while discouraging others from monopolizing the discussion. When you teach social skills by watching kids socially relate and then add ideas, it is difficult to get your less talkative students to join in and learn.

- With thinksheets, you can more easily encourage generalization of the social concepts outside the classroom or group. Thinksheets are easy to share with other stakeholders in the child's life, such as parents or therapists, so these people can reinforce the same concepts across a range of environments. This is important! Teaching Social Thinking and related skills involves using specific language-based concepts to explain the abstract expectations of the social world. When all parents and teachers use the same language to define and discuss these concepts, our teachings carry over between situations and environments.

Do the thinksheet lessons need to be introduced sequentially?

The thinksheets are roughly organized by categories, but you will find many of the categories overlap. They do not need to be presented in the order they appear in this book. However, you will find that many of the thinksheets relate to others that are included in the same chapter. We encourage you to use thinksheets as they are relevant to your teachings.

Can I share the thinksheets in this book?

The thinksheets are meant to be shared, within certain parameters. While this material is copyrighted and the book can't be copied and/or shared in its entirely or the materials posted to the Internet or a school's intranet, you can photocopy *select* thinksheets (or reproduce from files on the CD) to use *in-classroom* or *in-clinic* with your students and other stakeholders who are working one-on-one or living with the students with whom you work. This could include the student's parents, a service provider working with a student, a counselor, or a therapist.

When the thinksheets are shared in any manner, proper attribution is a must. Each thinksheet has a footnote citing the copyright to Think Social Publishing, Inc. and our website, www.socialthinking.com. It is important that this information stays intact. If you create your own Social Thinking thinksheets to share with your students based on information in this or other books or articles we have published, an attribution to our work is also needed, such as "Adapted from the Social Thinking® teaching framework created by Michelle Garcia Winner; www.socialthinking.com." Under no circumstances can any of the thinksheets, any variations of them, or any of your own adaptations of our work, be offered for sale. They are meant only for direct use, at no cost, with your own students.

What other information is available to help teach the concepts explained in the thinksheets at a deeper level?

Teaching Social Thinking and related social skills involves learning about the complex process we all use to communicate and share space with others. Books that effectively explain these concepts to parents and teachers can be found on our website, www.socialthinking.com:

- *Thinking About YOU Thinking About ME, 2nd edition* (Winner, 2007). This book has been referred to as the "bible" of Social Thinking in that it explains the core concepts of social relatedness in a user-friendly way for parents and teachers to explore.

- ***Think Social! A Social Thinking Curriculum for School-Age Students*** (Winner, 2005) takes the core concepts introduced in the above-mentioned book and teaches many of them through a detailed curriculum. A focus of this book is teaching the Social Thinking Vocabulary concepts through specific curriculum lessons. Crooke, Hendrix, and Rachman (2008) published research on the progress they noted from teaching these core vocabulary concepts.

- ***Social Behavior Mapping*** (Winner, 2007) is a teaching tool not explicitly discussed in *Social Thinking Thinksheets,* but it is effective with students in this tween to teen age range. It helps students understand how one's behavior impacts how others think and feel (based on it being expected or unexpected), how those thoughts and feelings produce reactions in others, which in turn affects how one thinks and feels about oneself. *Social Behavior Mapping* has been used widely with mainstream students to help them learn more about the social–emotional connection.

- ***Social Fortune or Social Fate: A Social Thinking Graphic Novel Map for Social Quest Seekers*** (Crooke and Winner, 2011). This book helps students gain ownership of their own social problem solving through further teaching of concepts introduced in *Social Behavior Mapping.*

- ***Why Teach Social Thinking? Questioning Our Assumptions About What It Means to Learn Social Skills*** (Winner, 2013) is a provocative discussion about the connections among social thinking, academic success, and later success in life as an adult. Through 12 questions, Winner explores the complex development of our social minds, how we view social intelligence, and the common assumptions about social learning that impact the way we teach students. Includes best-practice guidelines for teaching Social Thinking concepts and a downloadable study guide.

- ***Thinksheets for Teaching Social Thinking and Related Social Skills*** (Winner, 2005) is another collection of thinksheets that are mostly different from the ones included in this book. While some of the chapter headings are similar, and the material is geared mostly for students aged eight into young adulthood, there is much to teach and many different ways to teach the same concepts. It has a particularly good section on how we learn to change our behaviors by moving from self-awareness to self-control. (This book was previously titled *Worksheets for Teaching Social Thinking and Related Social Skills.*)

- ***Socially Curious and Curiously Social*** (Winner and Crooke, 2011) is geared to high-functioning teens and young adults to help explain shifting social emotional expectations as we grow up. Parents and teachers also benefit from reviewing these hands-on materials, giving them the opportunity to learn to "speak the same language" with their students. Many schools have adopted this book for teaching Social Thinking courses in high schools and for use by college counselors.

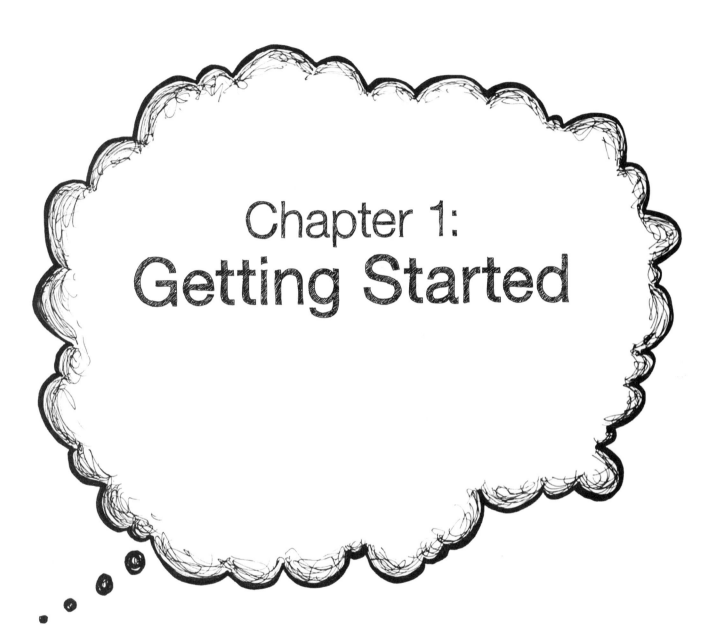

Incorporating Social Thinking into the Regular Education Classroom for Students in Early Adolescence

Introduction to Challenges Faced by Some Students

Some students have challenges beyond the academic curriculum, particularly those who have diagnostic labels that imply difficulties with impulsivity and relating socially to others.

Although it's essential that students constantly monitor and regulate their social behavior throughout the school day, little direct information is provided about the hidden social curriculum (HSC) or what we describe to the students as the "hidden rules." While the school day offers students a range of academic curricula, the day has an even more intense HSC that underlies success in any environment, whether in science, English, the cafeteria, or hanging out during breaks, etc.

An example of the HSC can be observed at any moment of the day; there are social rules and expectations for lining up after recess, raising one's hand in class, working as part of a small group on a class project, listening while the teacher talks, joining groups on the playground, eating lunch with peers, asking for help, and more. The HSC is an overwhelmingly complex set of expectations that shifts quickly and efficiently to keep the school day functioning smoothly, allowing many students to be educated in a group. Without the HSC, social chaos would dominate, and teachers would not be able to teach.

The ability to innately interpret and regulate oneself around the HSC is part of what is called "normal development." Neurotypical children start to intuitively understand the social structures and intentions of others from birth. With relatively little teaching of the explicit social rules, neurotypical children learn how to read the intentions of others, develop communication for commenting and questioning (to share people's worlds), and engage in complex play by sharing imaginations. As they then approach school age, they learn how to use all this information to sit in a classroom, stifle their responses, and learn lessons (as part of a large group) that are not always of great interest to them. As they grow toward middle school age, they're also expected to critically think through their own opinions but remain flexible enough to accept other people's differing opinions. We also see the HSC develop into managing organizational skills so the group can work together efficiently. By the time students approach high school, it's expected that they have learned how to self-advocate, problem solve, and develop social networks, all critical skills for coping with their emerging adulthoods.

Thankfully, the majority of students learn all of this intuitively, with a few bumps and bruises along the way that naturally enforce following the HSC. However, there is a group of students with a learning disability in social thinking or social intelligence that makes learning the HSC quite challenging. Some of the diagnostic labels that represent this type of learning disability include students on the autism spectrum (Autism, Pervasive Developmental Disorder—Not Otherwise Specified, Asperger Syndrome), and those with ADHD, Nonverbal Learning Disability, Hyperlexia, Social Anxiety, and other murky undiagnosed kids that stand out in the group. While some of these students may present with very obvious social challenges in that they're extremely aloof and odd, other students with these challenges may actually look like neurotypical students who misbehave in class.

Brighter students, those with solid intelligence and good language skills but who also have challenges in social thinking, are difficult to diagnose given that they often do well on formal tests. While formalized tests provide strong structure through their development and administration, a significant part of the very real challenges in learning the HSC is that it exists without clearly defined structures. As parents and teachers, we rarely label the rules encased in the HSC; we just expect that students should know and abide by them. For students who cannot easily intuit these expectations, the result is possible confusion, anger, depression, anxiety, and lack of healthy peer relations—further distancing them from their peer group.

In addition to the burden of not intuitively understanding how to cope in the many contexts that span the school day, these students often find that their challenges regarding social interpretation also seep into related challenges in their schoolwork. The majority of these students demonstrate some level of related difficulty with reading comprehension of literature (even if they're excellent decoders), making inferences across their curricula, efficiently summarizing the main idea, cognitively organizing information to express ideas through written expression, and developing organizational structures for managing homework assignments. Some also have significant difficulty with inferring meaning in abstract math equations such as word problems and algebra. The connection of how a social problem merges into academic problems, even for many academically "bright students," is more deeply explained in the ILAUGH Model of Social Thinking, which is further described on our organization's website (*www.socialthinking.com*) via a number of free articles and related books (Winner, 2000, 2005, 2007). It's no wonder that so many of our students are described by their parents as "bright but (socially) clueless."

Exploring Educational Strategies for the Regular Education Environment

Helping students with social cognitive challenges requires you, the teacher, to fully understand that the student has a deficit in his or her intuitive ability to "crack the social code" in your classroom. Thus, the job of the mainstream teacher is to help support the student's learning by helping to demystify some of the hidden social curriculum. Another way to think about the HSC is to explore the "hidden rules" that are embedded into every moment of the day in school, on the playground, in the cafeteria. Further information on learning how to think through the hidden rules can be found in the book, *The Hidden Curriculum: Practical Solutions for Understanding Unstated Rules in Social Situations* (Myles, Trautman, and Schelvan, 2004).

To even begin to follow these hidden rules, students need to learn how to consider the perspective of those around them, make educated guesses, and understand how to "read" and respond to the organizational structures. It's not expected that the classroom teacher will actually create the lessons to prepare students with social cognitive learning challenges to succeed in the regular education classroom. As long as the student qualifies for IEP or 504 services, this is the job of the special educator, paraprofessional, speech-language pathologist, occupational therapist, school psychologist, and behaviorist. If you as a teacher feel that a student can't participate effectively in the regular education class due to difficulties participating in the HSC, it's important that the student be assessed for special education so he or she can begin to receive these more specialized services. If a student is receiving these special education supports, it is also important for the regular education teacher to collaborate with the special education team so the student has consistency with the information he or she is learning.

It's the job of the regular education teacher to try and make the HSC more explicit and less hidden in the mainstream classroom. The good news is that by helping students with social cognitive learning challenges to understand the HSC, you will also help your whole classroom to better understand the importance and structure of the social rules not only in school but in society. Below, a Social Thinking Vocabulary© is defined that can be easily used in the regular education classroom during teachable moments.

Many teachers today talk about the fact that as our society changes and parents are not as available to work directly with the students on social behavior, the classroom teacher finds that he or she has to work harder at getting all students to carry out the concept of "respect" in the class, especially with older students. The lessons included here apply to ALL!

Using a Social Thinking Vocabulary in Your Classroom with ALL Students

The first step in teaching students to think socially is to introduce them to a new set of vocabulary concepts. The purpose of the *Social Thinking Vocabulary* is to *explicitly* label aspects of social behavior that have been previously *assumed* to be tangible for all students. While we encourage the special education team members to introduce these concepts to the students through activities and games, it's critical that the regular education teacher use this vocabulary during the "teachable moments" so that students can understand how to *apply the information in real time*. The concepts described below are very basic, so basic that the biggest challenge is often in realizing that these actually need to be taught. Do not assume that your student does not need these concepts because she is "smart" and has a good vocabulary. Students with social cognitive learning challenges must be guided back to the social basics to make sure they have the building blocks in place to deal with the increasing social complexities of the world as they age. Research has been published on the effectiveness of using Social Thinking vocabulary to teach social concepts and related skills with children (Crooke, Hendrix, and Rachman, 2008).

Social thinking happens EVERYWHERE so we need to use these concepts everywhere. It's important for teachers on yard duty or working in the cafeteria as well as parents and family members to infuse these concepts into the students' recreational and home life.

The following descriptions of many of the Social Thinking concepts will be helpful to introduce to the students.

A Brief Review of Some Social Thinking Vocabulary Terms

More Social Thinking vocabulary terms are taught through curriculum lessons in **Think Social, A Social Thinking Curriculum for School Age Students** (Winner, 2005). *Not all concepts reviewed below relate to thinksheets included in this book.*

To help students understand that they can represent two different types of people when in a group or classroom, we use the following two terms. Being a **Thinking of Others** person means you think about others and cooperate. If you are a **Just Me** person, you think only about yourself and what you want to do, with little regard for other people's needs.

Thinking with your eyes means using your eyes to figure out what nonverbal messages others are sending. This is accomplished through reading others' eye-gaze directions, facial expressions, and body language. "Thinking with your eyes" encourages students to be more active listeners; it's more descriptive than saying "look at me" or "use good eye contact."

Flexible thinking and flexible brain refer to having the mental flexibility to interpret verbal and nonverbal information based on different points of view or different contexts. This is the opposite of having a **rigid brain** or **rock brain,** which alludes to when a student uses a strict set of rules or has a limited understanding of the world and cannot interpret subtly different meanings in language, expression, play, or intention.

Keeping your body and brain in the group involves understanding that our bodies need to look interested and connected to the group, and our brains need to keep thinking about what the group is thinking about to participate in the group. We also teach that people can see when your body or brain does not appear to be a part of the group.

Your body rolled out of the group means the student's body is turned or has physically moved away from the group, and it appears that the student's body is too far away from the group to be an active participant. At times this means that the student is just one step further back from the rest of the group. A student does not have to be physically far away from the group to send the impression that he is not or does not want to be in the group. You can also ask your class, *"Whose bodies are in the group? Whose bodies look like they're out of the group?"* This helps to develop self-awareness of other people's perceptions about physical presence and physical distance.

Your brain rolled out of the group means that the student's brain is distracted from what the group is doing; the other people in the group notice that he does not appear to be mentally working as part of the group even though his body is still in the group! You can also ask your class, "Whose brain is in the group? Whose brain looks like it's out of the group?" This helps to develop self-awareness of other people's perceptions about each person's mental presence in a group.

Blue thoughts *(good thoughts)* ***and red thoughts*** *(not so good/weird thoughts)* refer to how our actions, words, and even physical dress or hygiene create good thoughts and weird thoughts in others' brains (that is, the impressions that we make). All people have good thoughts and weird thoughts during a day. People remember the thoughts they have about someone else. If the student primarily imparts good thoughts (blue thoughts) in people's minds, people will generally think good thoughts about her. If a person imparts mostly "weird thoughts" (red thoughts), that is what people mostly remember. Behaving really well after producing a lot of weird thoughts or weird behaviors still leaves people remembering the weird thoughts. Teachers usually teach this lesson by using red and blue Popsicle sticks. When a student is working well, the teacher puts a blue stick in a Dixie cup in front of the student; if a student is doing odd behaviors or saying unexpected comments, the teacher puts a red stick in the cup. Sometimes the students want to hide the red sticks they've received, and the teacher explains that even when the red sticks are taken out of the cup, they are still in our memory. The only way to truly fade them out is to fill our memory with more blue thoughts.

Whole body listening: The whole body (eyes, ears, mouth, hands, feet, shoulders, bottom, and brain) needs to be focused on the group in order to listen and to show others that you are listening.

Following hidden rules: Not all rules are clearly announced. Most rules in our world are rules people figure out through observation and experience. For example, one hidden rule is that you are usually supposed to leave your shoes on in school even though you take them off at home. If you are not sure of the rules, you can ask someone.

Doing what is "expected" refers to a range of hidden rules in every situation. We have to figure out what those rules are and then follow them to keep other people feeling good about us. Following the hidden rules is "doing what is expected."

Doing what is "unexpected" refers to failing to follow a set of rules, hidden or stated, in a specific environment. Not following these rules is unexpected behavior.

Making a **"smart guess"** is taking information you already know and making an educated guess based on that information. We usually use the words "smart guess" with younger students when we want to teach them how to make guesses. We teach that the teachers in school usually ask questions that require "smart guesses," ones based on information the students have already learned.

A **"wacky guess"** is making a guess when you have absolutely no information to help you figure out what the guess should be. In school, teachers rarely ask for this type of guessing unless students are playing a wacky game.

Friend files are a visual way to help students understand that we all are continually learning information about others and filing it in an organized way in our brains so we can recall it later when we see those people again.

Social wondering *(wondering about others)* is a concept to help students begin to explore the idea that we're supposed to have a social curiosity about others and that we can NEVER know everything there is to know about someone. Social wondering means you have a thought about someone's experience or beliefs and then you ask a question or make a comment related to your thought. For example, "I wonder what you like to do at Disneyland?"

Asking questions to the people they're talking to about these people refers to asking questions that focus on the interests or thoughts of the person or people to whom we are relating.

Asking people questions simply refers to asking questions of people. The focus is on the interests or thoughts of that person or those people.

"Baiting" or "bridging" questions are questions you ask people to try to get them to talk about what you want to talk about (e.g., "Did anyone go to Hawaii this summer?"). The student may ask this because she went to Hawaii and wants to talk about it.

Add-a-thought: When talking to others, we consider how their experiences relate to our experiences. We then "add our own thoughts" to help connect our lives to their lives. For example, if I say, "I went out to dinner last night," an add-a-thought comment you might say is, "We saw a movie last night."

Figuring out other people's plans involves observing people's physical actions or comments to determine what they plan to do next. We can also start to figure out what people are planning to do by interpreting the subtle meanings in their actions and language; this is a higher level skill.

Four steps of communication: When communicating with a person face-to-face, communication begins with:
1. Thinking about others and others thinking about you
2. Creating a physical presence
3. Thinking with your eyes
4. Using language to relate to others

The **Social Fake** is used to demonstrate interest in someone else's topic that you do not find inherently fascinating. Students, at times, need to learn that they can fake it through the boring moment, rather than tell people they're not interested in what the other person is talking about. They may be surprised to find something interesting after all.

Tolerating the boring moment refers to a set of socially acceptable behaviors that we demonstrate when we're not interested in what the group is doing at that moment but we still hang in there and do not distract other people.

Whopping topic change is a comment that is completely disconnected to what has been previously said. The listener cannot figure out how the speaker arrived at the "whopping topic change comment," also referred to humorously as the "WTC."

Tiny problem vs. big (earthquake) problem: Understanding that problems differ in severity helps one react appropriately to these problems. We need to directly teach some students to better explore the size of their problem before reacting to it. Some students react to all problems as if they're "earthquakes."

The rules change: The rules that students are taught during their childhood change so they must undo some of the lessons taught to them as they age. For example, apologizing by simply saying, "I am sorry" is okay for an eight-year-old, but by fifteen years of age you have to show you're sorry through your actions in addition to your words. It's also okay for a five-year-old to throw himself on the floor when he thinks something is funny, but it's unusual for a fourth grader to do this. To help a student learn that a behavior that was once acceptable is no longer acceptable now that he or she is older, we explain that "the rules have changed."

Many other concepts can be defined and used actively in social situations. The key to defining a concept is to make it educational rather than purely punitive. Giving the concept a name or label and then actively teaching the meaning of the concept gives consistency and familiarity to the concept. Enjoy creating some of your own.

. . . .

Figuring Out How We Communicate

The development of social skills requires abstract/flexible thinking as well as the ability to self-monitor and self-correct one's own skills during the communicative process. To foster improvement, we break down the Social Thinking concepts into smaller more concrete ideas to help students develop cognitive and self-awareness strategies.

While the student may have more issues than are described below, we must prioritize what to work on based on his or her current stage of development and overall abilities. Some specific therapeutic techniques you can use to work on these categories are described in my book, *Thinking About YOU Thinking About ME, 2nd edition* (Winner, 2007, *www.socialthinking.com*).

Four Steps of Communication

1. ***Thinking about others and how they think about me:*** All of our work on understanding how their verbal and nonverbal communication impacts the way others think about them. As part of working on this concept, we explore what it means to work in a group as opposed to working on your own, the students' perceptions of others, and then how to self-monitor how others perceive them. With older students we work more directly on understanding the complexities of taking into account different perspectives. This is a slowly evolving process of learning, but we do see students make gains in their understanding of this highly thoughtful social process.

2. ***Body proximity, body language, and body movement:*** Our bodies help people to anticipate our desire to interact with them or possibly our lack of desire. Our students work to increase their awareness of what their body movements, and those of others, convey about what each person might be thinking. We then work on developing related skills that are relevant for the student.

3. ***Eyes have thoughts:*** The expression "eye contact" encourages students to look at another person but it does not help them to learn about how eyes are "a window into the soul." Instead, we teach the concept that you "think with your eyes" and then we help the students to learn how to read some of the possible thoughts, emotions, and intentions of others based on what another person might be looking at. We also help students to understand that people look at the student's eye gaze to determine his or her thoughts, intentions, and more.

4. ***Use of language to show people our thoughts:*** We explore the concept that language only makes sense to other people when the speaker is thinking about

them (viewing it from their perspective). For example, it's difficult to tell a story if the speaker doesn't think about the knowledge or experiences of the person to whom he is talking. We then teach students the different components of language that help them to be perceived as friendly, informative, and thoughtful to others.

· ·

Teaching Social Thinking

Remember that Social Thinking happens EVERYWHERE: at home, at school, out in the community, and other places. It is not something that only happens during breaks in the school day or when kids are relaxing at home.

Below are some concepts you may want to explore through the use of these thinksheets with your students:

- Social laws—What are our social laws for our group? How can we take care of each others' feelings every week and make other people have good thoughts about us?

- Review the four steps of communication—how can we apply these when we're in group? Make a collective poster as a group.

- What are each student's strengths and weaknesses academically?

- What are each student's strengths and weaknesses socially?

- What does it mean to be flexible? How can we actively teach our students to be flexible in everyday life?

- What is an impression? What impression do our students make to others through their social behaviors including what they say, how they say it, how they look, and so on. Do they know they make impressions through their actions or inaction?

- What types of groups hang out together at school during break times? Who do your students see themselves connecting to/making friends with? Are they part of a group or do they only stay by themselves? How can they learn to be part of a group, even if it is a very small group?

- How is bullying and teasing managed in your school and/or home? What makes some students a target? How can students cope with others who are mean to them? How do students distinguish between those who are genuinely mean versus those who are engaging in friendly teasing? What is the responsibility of adults when students target one person?

- How are we teaching students to stick up for themselves? *(Self advocacy)*

- What does friendship mean to your student and/or different students? Do they understand there are different types of friendships: friends, acquaintances, real friends, others around us, and mean people? How does trust relate to different levels of friendship? What does it look like?

- How can our students learn to build selected friendships? How can they learn to just appear friendly even if they don't want to have a lot of friends?

- How can we teach the "hidden rules" more explicitly? Hidden rules need to become less "hidden" in our homes, schools, and community for our students with social learning challenges. What are some hidden rules at your school, home, or classroom? Can you have your students explore sharing the hidden rules as they detect them? They can do this during discussions of social behavior as they explore how we think about different perspectives and behavior as part of the language arts curriculum.

- A teaching concept called Social Behavior Mapping© is not reviewed in this book, but is ideal for pre-adolescents and adolescents. Please refer to my book **Social Behavior Mapping** (Winner, 2007) to learn more about this concept. Social Behavior Maps explore how some behaviors are expected and others are unexpected based on the hidden rules for a situation. Expected behaviors tend to make others feel good. Those good feelings usually result in the person who did the expected behavior being treated in a more positive way. That in turn results in this person feeling good about how he is treated by others. Unexpected behaviors produced by a person tend to make others feel uncomfortable, resulting in the person who produced the unexpected behaviors being treated badly, leading to that person feeling mad at others. Social Behavior Maps can be used for understanding how characters react and respond to others in books of literature as well as for studying how people react and respond to each other at school, at home, and in the community.

- What are the social goals for each student at home and school? We often don't think of children as having social goals and action plans, but we should!

- Goals are ideas we *think* about achieving. Action plans are things we *do* to help us achieve our goals. What lessons will be used to teach students how they can participate in the action plans to help them achieve their goals?

- Track your student's Social Thinking progress—students do best at reaching their goals or at least show improvement when they're taught to self-monitor their own social behavior. Many thinksheets in this book encourage students to learn to self-monitor their Social Thinking and related social skills.

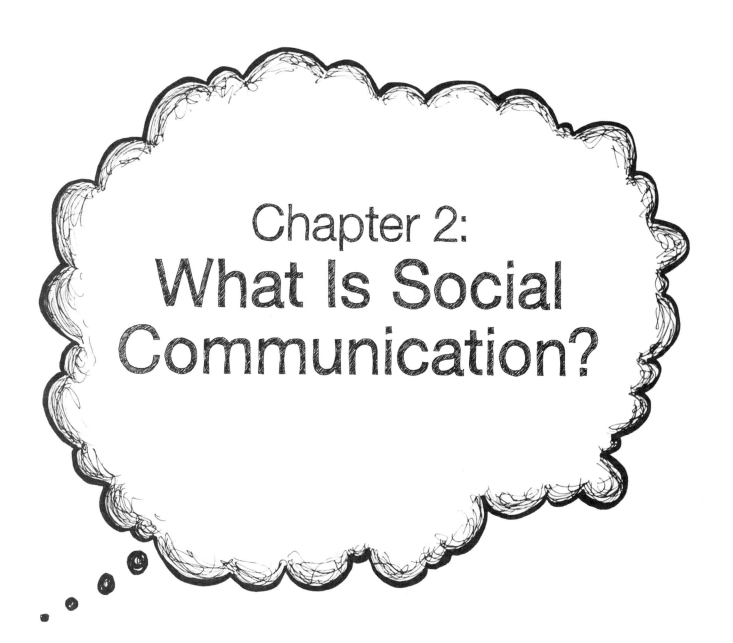

Chapter 2:
What Is Social
Communication?

Why Do We Have Lessons on Social Thinking?

Our class does lessons on Social Thinking. Sometimes I'm a little confused about why we have to have these.

Keeping track of our own thoughts and those of others is not easy. Then we have to try and figure out how best to respond to people. Our brains are supposed to do this really quickly—in less than one second!! Because so much is demanded from the social learning part of our brains, it gets complicated really quickly.

Every single person on the face of the earth messes up social interactions some of the time. They are too complicated to do correctly all of the time! But, figuring out how to be with people is important! Learning about Social Thinking helps with all of this. Being a better social thinker helps us to make friends, problem solve, and feel relaxed around others, even when we're not talking with them.

The weird thing about learning about Social Thinking and social skills is that if you know people who say they already know how to do this all perfectly, they're probably not being quite honest. So the lessons help not just you, but everyone!

Below is a description of some Social Thinking ideas. *Circle the response that you relate to the best.*

1. **Eyes have thoughts:** My eyes have thoughts. The direction of my eyes lets other people know what I'm thinking about. When I look at someone during a conversation, the person knows that I am thinking about him.

    I'm just okay at this skill.   I need some help.   I'm really good at this!

2. **Tone of voice and volume of voice:** My tone of voice sends a message to other people about how I'm feeling. It's important to use the appropriate tone of voice in certain situations and avoid using a nagging or rude tone of voice.

    I'm just okay at this skill.   I need some help.   I'm really good at this!

3. **Thinking about other people:** When I'm in the group, I need to keep thinking about the group. If my brain rolls away from the group, I'm showing other people that I'm not thinking about them. Other people don't want to be around me if I don't think about them.

    I'm just okay at this skill.   I need some help.   I'm really good at this!

4. **Having a flexible brain:** Having a flexible brain is important so that I can show others that I can accept change. It also means I can change my thoughts to help the group problem solve and make decisions.

    I'm just okay at this skill.   I need some help.   I'm really good at this!

5. **My body makes connections:** My body lets other people know how I'm feeling and what I'm thinking about. If I slouch down in my chair, I'm letting other people know that I am not listening to them or I'm tired. I need to be aware of the message my body sends other people at all times!

I'm just okay at this skill.   I need some help.   I'm really good at this!

6. **Listening skills:** I can use my body to show other people that I am listening to them and thinking about what is being said. Some of my good listening skills are looking at the speakers and giving them my full attention or giving them feedback to let them know that I am thinking about what they're saying. I can also show that I am listening to a person by watching out for interruptions and waiting until the speaker is done talking.

I'm just okay at this skill.   I need some help.   I'm really good at this!

7. **Thinking of Others:** Am I a Just-Me or a Thinking-of-Others kind of kid? Do I only talk about what I want to talk about, or do I think about what other people might want to talk about?

I'm just okay at this skill.   I need some help.   I'm really good at this!

8. **Using my words to make connections:** I can use my words to make connections with other people. I can ask questions about other people to let them know that I am thinking about them. If I don't talk to them, they may think I am unfriendly. If I only talk about what I want to talk about, they might think I am being a Just Me!

I'm just okay at this skill.   I need some help.   I'm really good at this!

9. **Good thoughts and weird thoughts:** I want people to have good thoughts about me. If I do what is expected, other people will have good thoughts about me. If I do what is unexpected, other people might have bad or weird thoughts about me.

I'm just okay at this skill.   I need some help.   I'm really good at this!

10. **Adding thoughts to the group:** When I am having a conversation in a group, I want to add my thoughts to the group. This lets other people know that I am thinking about what they're saying, and I am staying connected to the group!

I'm just okay at this skill.   I need some help.   I'm really good at this!

Social Thinking Toolbox

We all know that tools are used to build, create, connect, fix, change, tighten, and loosen things, and on and on and on. We use different tools for different jobs. We use hammers to nail things together and pliers to pull things out. There are clamps to hold things, jacks that lift things, and sanders that make things smooth. Each tool has a special job, and without tools, we couldn't create, add, fix, change, tighten, or loosen things, and on and on and on.

We are learning about Social Thinking and, guess what? We use tools! Our tools are used to help us build relationships. We have very special tools for creating relationships, keeping relationships connected, and fixing, changing, tightening, and loosening relationships, and so on.

Our Social Thinking toolbox has tools like flexible thinking, thinking with our eyes, keeping our bodies connected, surviving the boring moment, doing the social fake, and more.

We will learn about lots of tools that we can use in all kinds of places (school, home, at a friend's house, in the grocery store, anyplace where there are people). To get really good at using any tool, whether it's a screwdriver or the four steps of communication, we need to practice using the tool A LOT! You'll learn new tools and then practice using them at home, at school, and in other places.

How many tools do you already have in your toolbox? Are there any missing or ones that don't get used enough?

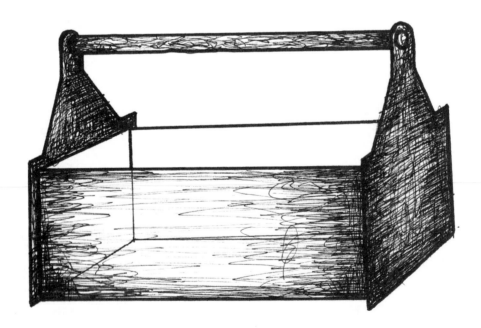

Four Steps of Communication to Become a Social Thinker

1. **Thinking about people and what they think and feel.**

   a. What are they interested in?
   b. What do they feel about what you're saying?
   c. What are you doing to show you're interested in them when they're talking?

2. **Being aware of your physical presence as well as the physical presence of others.**

   a. Your body position shows who you want to talk to or not talk to.
   b. Your body movements show what you plan to do next. Your body sends messages, even messages you didn't mean to send.
   c. Your body language and facial expression communicate to people how you feel about things or people around you.

3. **Using your eyes to think about others and what they're thinking about.**

   a. The direction of your eyes and other people's eyes lets people see what everyone might be thinking about.
   b. We use our eyes to help figure out how people feel, what people are thinking about, and if they're interested in us.

4. **Using your language to relate to others.**

   a. Talking about things that are interesting to others.
   b. Asking questions to find out about people and making comments to show interest in others.
   c. Adding your own thoughts to connect your experiences to other people's experiences.
   d. Adjusting your language to what the group or another person is talking about.

FOUR STEPS to BECOMING a SOCIAL THINKER

USING YOUR **BRAIN**
TO THINK ABOUT OTHERS

USING YOUR **EYES**
TO MAKE CONNECTIONS

USING YOUR **BODY**
TO MAKE CONNECTIONS

USING YOUR **WORDS**
TO MAKE CONNECTIONS

Social Thinking® *Thinksheets for Tweens and Teens*

Who's in the Spotlight?

Today, we'll play "Who's in the spotlight?" We'll shine the spotlight on the person talking and give that person **ALL** of our attention.

We'll practice **KEEPING OUR BRAIN THINKING ABOUT THE PERSON** (by thinking about what he or she is saying and picturing what he or she is talking about).

We'll practice **KEEPING OUR BODIES POINTED AT THE PERSON** (to show we're thinking about him or her).

We'll practice **THINKING ABOUT THE PERSON WITH OUR EYES** (by focusing our eyes on the person).

We'll practice **KEEPING OUR WORDS TALKING ABOUT WHAT THE PERSON IS TALKING ABOUT** (by adding comments and asking questions about what he or she is talking about).

When we give people ALL of our attention, they feel good about talking with us and will want to talk with us even more! How long can you keep your spotlight on other people?

Rate yourself on four different occasions:

1 = I need some help.   2 = I need to practice this skill.   3 = I am really good at this!

	Trial 1	Trial 2	Trial 3	Trial 4	Trial 5
I kept my BRAIN thinking about others.					
I kept my BODY pointed toward others.					
I kept my EYES thinking about others.					
I kept my WORDS thinking about others.					

Describe It with Language!

Let people know what you see inside of your head by putting the picture in their head through language.

People will never know how you experience things around you unless you tell them. We want to learn about each other!

. . . .

Tell people about your own experiences by describing to them:

1. The place:
Where was it?
What did it look like?
How did the place make you feel?

2. The people:
Who were they?
What was their age, gender, and grade?
How did they feel?

3. What was happening?
What were people doing?
What was happening around them?
How were they feeling about what they do?

4. Was there a problem or a possible problem?
What was the problem?
What happened next?
What could have been the problem if people didn't pay attention to fixing things?

Goin' Fishin'

Having a conversation with someone is like goin' fishin'! We want to think about the person. We need to be able to "bait" the person by using our words. Once we have them "hooked," we have to keep reeling them in, to keep them interested.

Going fishing is not an easy task, as any fisherman will tell you. A lot of preparation is involved—you have to find the right location, have the right bait and line, patience, and be aware of how the fish is responding. It's just like this when you have a conversation—you need to prepare before you can bait your fish (person) and reel them in.

You need to:

1. Think about the person: What do you remember about the person (*reach into your memory tackle box*) and what are the person's interests? What is he or she interested in talking about?

2. **Point your body** toward the person (*or fish, hee hee!*). Keep your body close to the group (*school of fish*) or person (*fish*) and show with your body language that you're interested in the conversation by using a friendly tone, shaking your head when other people talk, etc. (*Here little fishy...*)

3. **Eyes:** Keep looking at the person with your eyes. Don't stare! The fish might dart away.

4. **Language (bait):** Finally, now you need to use your words to communicate with that person or others! When in a successful conversation, you could think, "I got one," versus seeing the person as "the one that got away."

So how do you do this? Well, first you have to take a look into your tackle box. You think of it like a MEMORY TACKLE BOX. In your memory tackle box, you can store information you remember about that person so that you can use it to bait your line.

For example, if you see your friend John walking up, and you know he went to Tahoe last weekend, you could bait your fishing line with this question:

Hi, John! How was your trip to Tahoe?

What else could you say next to bait and support what we're talking about?

Keep him "on the line" with another question or related comment. When the conversation is over, it's time to gently "release" him.

GOIN' FISHIN' When Hanging Out with Others

Hanging out with others is like goin' fishin'! While we are around others, we want to think about them. So, we need to be able to "bait" the person by using our words, and then once we have them "hooked" we have to keep reeling them in—to keep them interested and having fun with us. *You need to:*

1. **Think about the person:** What do you remember about the person (*reach into your memory tackle box*) and what are their interests? What are they interested in doing?

2. **Body Language and Space:** Point your body towards the person (*or fish*), keep your body close to the group (*school of fish*) or person (*fish*), and show with your body language that you are interested in the game or activity by using a "friendly" posture or facial expression, shaking your head when they are talking, etc. (Here little fishy...)

3. **Eyes:** Keep looking at (thinking about) the person with your eyes. Don't stare! The fish might dart away.

4. **Language (Bait):** Finally, you can use your words to show others you're interested.

Here are some ideas for fish bait questions to use when you're hanging out with others:

How about_____?

What do you think of_____?

What's your idea? Or, What do you want to do?

Here are some fish bait comments to use when you are hanging out with others:

Keep him "on the line" with another question, another action, or related comments.
When you're done hanging out, it's time to gently "release" him.

Goin' Fishin': Putting It All Together

Hanging out or talking with someone is like goin' fishin'! How is that possible? Well, when we talk to others, we can keep people interested and wanting to keep talking to us with the words we use *(words are like the bait.)*

Let's look at the four steps of communication and then compare these to what a fisherman must do to catch fish.

Four Steps of Communication	Social-Thinkerman	Four Steps to Catching the Big Fish	Fisherman
1. Thinking about others		1. Thinking about his or her fish	
2. Body language and personal space		2. What does his or her body need to do?	
3. Eyes to think about others		3. Eyes to think about his or her fish	
4. Using language (bait) to think about others		4. Using his bait to catch his or her fish	

Now let's practice putting it all together.

For example, if you see your friend Mark sitting in the lobby and you know he went to Disneyland for spring break, you could bait your fishing line with this question:

Hi, Mark. How was your trip to Disneyland?

What else could you say next to bait and support the topic to keep him reeled in?

Choosing Your Words Carefully!

It's not that you can never talk about certain topics. It's that you have to talk about them carefully! What we are and are not allowed to talk about can be very, very subtle. This is where you have to monitor your comments while other people think about what you might be saying!

To do this you have to self-monitor your behavior, which means you watch yourself while you talk with or just hang out near others. There are very subtle differences in bait and brag, bait and comment, and bait and support.

Bait and brag (This is not highly recommended as a strategy to encourage success!)
This is where you introduce the topic and then tell people how wonderful you are!

- I got so many new clothes this weekend and they were all from really nice, expensive stores.

- I exercised this weekend each day for at least an hour. I hiked, played basketball, and went snowboarding. I feel so good.

- I had a test so I studied a whole bunch. I think I got an "A." How do you think you did?

- I stayed home and read some books. I read about one book every two days. I think books are much more interesting than people.

Bait and comment (This strategy helps you to introduce a topic to others.)
This is where you introduce the topic, but then you just talk about it. You provide information that does not make you look fabulous.

- I went shopping this weekend at the mall.

- I exercised outdoors this weekend a lot. I was so glad it didn't rain during the day.

- I studied a bunch for a test. I hate tests.

- I read some books while on vacation. I read a really interesting science fiction book.

Bait and support (This strategy is usually pretty successful.)
This is where you introduce the topic, but then you want to find out about how other people think.

- I went shopping this weekend at the Stanford Mall. Do you like to go there?

- I exercised outdoors this weekend a lot. What did you do?

- Did you worry much about the test today in math? You seem really good in that class.

- I read some books over vacation. Do you like to read?

Bait and lie (not recommended!!)
When you introduce a topic and then lie about what happened or didn't happen to make yourself look better to that person.

Can you think of some examples?

1. Going shopping at the mall:

2. Exercising this weekend:

3. Studying for a test:

4. Reading books over vacation:

. . . .

Bait and getting flung overboard
When you introduce a topic and you give too much information at one time.

Can you think of some examples?

1. Going shopping at the mall:

2. Exercising this weekend:

3. Studying for a test:

4. Reading books over vacation:

Social Thinking® Thinksheets for Tweens and Teens   © 2011 Think Social Publishing, Inc. • www.socialthinking.com

Keeping 'em Hooked

When you talk with others, it's important to remember to keep 'em hooked. *Here's how you can do this!*

. . . .

1. Pick a topic you think the other person would be interested in or a topic you know both of you like to talk about.

2. Don't bore the person by doing an "ALL ME ALL THE TIME," such as talking about your own interests or talking too long.

3. Make two or three comments, and then ask the other person a question about whatever you're talking about. Every time you ask the person a question, you "hook" him and bring him back into the conversation.

4. Watch the person's face to make sure he is still interested. If you see interest fading, change the topic and HOOK the person all over again!

. . . .

Let's give it a try! Think of a topic you think your PARTNER is interested in and write it in the first box. Next, write down your opening line (The HOOK!) in the second box. Okay, now you're ready to go fishing!

Find your partner and try it out.

Topic:	The Hook:

Keeping People Reeled In!

You have been learning about how to be a social thinker when you're around others. When you think about it, you are a SOCIAL THINKER any time you're around others. Let's take a look at some situations and use the *Four Steps of Communication* to explore how to keep others interested and feeling good when they're around you.

In a group: How do you keep people reeled in with your—

Thinking:_____

Body presence and personal space:_____

Eyes:_____

Language:_____

Working on a group project: How do you keep others reeled in with your—

Thinking:_____

Body presence and personal space:_____

Eyes:_____

Language:_____

Hanging out with others: How do you keep others reeled in with your—

Thinking:_____

Body presence and personal space:_____

Eyes:_____

Language:_____

Keep Fishing While You Hang Out

You learn how to keep thinking about others with your body and your words while you're hanging out with them. When you are with someone else, you have a job! Your job is to keep the other person WANTING to hang out with you! One important way you can do this is by adding your thoughts about what you're doing. Think of it like you're being a FISHERMAN and the other kids are the fish; you have to keep them REELED in on your line so they don't swim away!

. . . .

Here are some ways to do this:

- Ask them what they're doing.

- Ask them if they have ideas about what to do. ("What do you think?")

- Add your thoughts about what you're doing.

- You can add some of your own thoughts or experiences.

- You can add a thought about how they're doing. (For example, if you're playing a video game, you can say "Nice job," or "You're taking the lead.")

- You can compliment the other person. (You can say something nice like: "You're really good at this game," or "Nice throw.")

. . . .

If a friend is at your house and he says he's bored playing the video game you like, what could you do to keep him reeled in so he'll want to continue to hang out with you?

Let's say you and your friend are hanging out at the park. What could you say to keep her REELED in to continue hanging out with you?

The Power of a Magnet

We are like magnets. We can do and say things with our body, eyes, and words that make people want to be around us (*to attract them*), or we can do things with our body, eyes, and words to push people away (*repel them*).

One thing it's great to work on is how we can attract people and why we want to do this. You have the power to be like a magnet and bring people close to you!

What are some things that you could do with your **eyes** that would *attract* (+) *people*?

_____

_____

What are some things that you could do with your **eyes** that would *push people away* (-)?

_____

_____

What are some things that you could do with your **body** that would *attract* (+) *people*?

_____

_____

What are some things that you could do with your **body** that would *push people away* (-)?

_____

_____

What are some things that you could say with your **words** that would *attract* (+) *people*?

_____

_____

What are some things that you could say with your **words** that would *push people away* (-)?

_____

_____

Magnetic Communication 1

ATTRACT others to the conversation	REPEL others from the conversation
Saying things that show that you know what your peers like or are interested in:	Being critical — negativity
	Not agreeing
Looking at peers	Arguing
	Interrupting
Maintaining your PHYSICAL PRESENCE so people know you want to be with them	Too much sarcasm
	Negative tone or attitude
ADD MORE:	Saying "nothing" in response to "What's new?"
	Saying "nothing" literally
	Rolling eyes
	Ignoring peers
	Being too serious
	Poking
	Timing of humor
	Repeating everything others say
	Talking about things that others aren't interested in

Magnetic Communication 2

Communication tends to attract people together like two magnets....It can also be the reverse...communication can also repel people away from each other. The way to keep communication attracting people and to keep the interaction going is to show that we are thinking about each other.

Once we start thinking about each other, we then realize that the ways to keep pulling us together (*magnetic attraction*) are to:

1. Think about each other (what we remember about them, why we are talking, why we are being social, etc.).
2. Use our bodies appropriately to show we want to speak to someone.
3. Use our eyes to think about the person we're talking to so we can keep learning information about them.
4. Use our words to keep them wanting to talk to us (keep them in our magnetic field) by talking about things in which they're interested. Or, if we're talking about our areas of interest, we don't talk for too long before we go onto another topic or something else.

Let's focus on the talking part of communicating with others today. We'll play a game where comments and questions are given points for creating the communication magnet!

Comments	Points		Your Points
Comments that support what people are talking about	+	20	
Comments that switch to a related idea you want to talk about	+	10	
Comments that are whopping topic changes	-	20	
Questions			
Questions that get more information about what the person is talking about	+	20	
Questions that bait people to talk about what you want to talk about	-	20	
Miscellaneous			
Obnoxious or mean comments that are insulting to others or hurtful	-	50	
Comments that are not appropriate for the people you are around	-	20	
Total			

The Whole Body Communicates!

We can use our WHOLE BODY to keep thinking about others when they're around us. When we're around others, we need to keep thinking about them with our EYES, EARS, BODY, BRAIN, and then we can use our WORDS! If we are not listening to them and thinking about what they're saying, we won't know what to say next or we might say something to scramble their brains (not on topic). Let's take a closer look at how our whole bodies help us.

Our eyes help us think about others by:

> Draw some listening eyes!

Our bodies help us think about others by:

> Draw a listening body!

Our ears help us think about others by:

> Draw some listening ears!

Our brains help us think about others by:

> Draw a thinking brain!

Finally, our WORDS help us think about others by:

If I can think about others using my whole body and my words. When I say things that show I am interested in what someone else just said, this typically makes people feel good about talking to me.

Write some words that show others we're thinking about what they're saying, while also helping that person to have good thoughts about me.

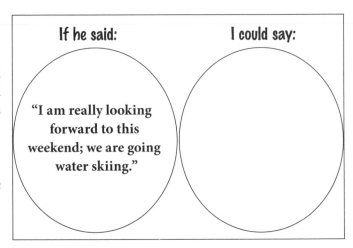

If he said:

"I am really looking forward to this weekend; we are going water skiing."

I could say:

Social Thinking® Thinksheets for Tweens and Teens

Physical Space?

Why is the space or distance between people so important when you interact with them? Personal space is really how an interaction begins! When you want to talk to someone or someone is trying to talk to you, you want the person to THINK that you're listening and interested, so you may get closer to the person or turn your shoulders so that you're facing him. This is as important as thinking about the person with your eyes.

How close should you be to someone when you're talking to the person?

_____

_____

How close should you be if you're playing a game with someone?

_____

_____

What if you're sitting down next to someone? How do you show the person with your body that you're interested and that you're listening?

_____

_____

Something as simple as the physical space between you and another person can SEND A MESSAGE. We can even communicate that we want to join a group just by standing next to the group. Isn't that amazing?

How are you with thinking about personal space when you're talking to others? *Give one example:*

_____

_____

_____

Whether you're about to go to school or you're heading out to be with a buddy, right now would be a great time to talk about how you'll try to think about others and make some good impressions. How could you try to make a good impression with others based on "space"?

1.

2.

Initiating Communication to Help Yourself!

Initiating communication means you are the one who begins to talk or communicate with someone else to let the person know that you need something or just to show that you want to be with him or her. You aren't waiting for someone to come up and ask if you need help or if you want to hang out together; you take the lead.

Initiating asking for help

What are some of the different situations you could be in when you would need to ask for help (self-initiated)?

_____

What is the difference between asking for help and asking for clarification?

_____

Do people only ask for help or need more explanation when they're having a "dumb moment"?

_____

How do you feel when you have to ask for help?

_____

How do you feel when you have to ask for clarification?

_____

How do you initiate asking for help in a classroom?

_____

Is there ever a bad time to ask for help? If so, when?

_____

Is it possible to ask for help too much? Why?

_____

How do you initiate asking for help when you're not in a classroom?

_____

What kind of help/clarification would you be asking for when not in class?

_____

Who do you ask for help?...in class? in the community?...at home?

_____

Initiating showing interest in another person

How do you initiate talking to a person that you want to play a game with or hang out with?

_____

Do you just start talking to a person or do you need to use your body to physically approach that person before you start talking?

_____

Initiating communication with another person involves more than just talking to them; you have to use your body and your eyes. Describe how the *four steps of communication* help you to initiate communication with another person.

_____

Try it...do a role play where you have to walk up to a person or a group to initiate communication.

How did you do using all four steps?

_____

_____

Which step do you think you need to work on the most to help make this easier for you?

_____

_____

Using Our Eyes

When we are around others, we have to be...**SOCIAL DETECTIVES**.

In other words, we need to use our eyes to look for clues just like a detective would look for clues to solve a crime. By using your eyes to look for clues, you will become better at THINKING OF OTHERS. How do we do that? What are some ways that using our eyes might show others that we are thinking about them?

. . . .

How do we use our *eyes* to make guesses when we talk to someone?

How do we use our *eyes* to make guesses about our teacher in the classroom?

How do we use our *eyes* to make guesses about our mom or dad when we're at home?

Making guesses with our *eyes* is only the first step. What should you do once you have made a guess about someone?

Guessed: Oh, this person keeps looking around while I'm talking to him.
Do?

Guessed: Oh, mom is not saying much during our conversation. I think she's bored with my topic.
Do?

Guessed: Oh, my teacher is mad because I kept talking and trying to ask questions.
Do?

Being the Social Detective and Figuring Out the Mystery

We are learning to be better Social Detectives to figure out what's happening around us so we know what to do or say. We do this with "thinking with our eyes" and finding the SMART clues to get the main idea. But at times our brain throws us off course by having us focus on small details in the picture that may result in us making a WACKY guess about what is going on. *For example*, if you look at a picture of people sitting together picnicking, clues that help you to make a smart guess about this include a picnic blanket, food spread out, and people sitting in a group together while they appear to eat. All those clues help you to build the main idea. However, you can look at the same picture and notice the different color tennis shoes people are wearing to the picnic. You may then say the picture is about wearing different color shoes. Over-focusing on this detail may lead you to make a wacky guess. Being a detective means figuring out what information is important for figuring out what people are doing or feeling and what information is irrelevant to the story, resulting in wacky summaries.

	Smart clues	Wacky clues	What happened?
Picture 1:			
Picture 2:			
Picture 3:			

Make the Guess

It is not easy to tell what others are thinking, so we have to try and make the best guess from all the clues. If we don't read the clues, we may hurt someone's feelings, make someone mad, or make someone have a really weird thought about us. When you're with others, you always have to be the SOCIAL DETECTIVE and figure out others' plans. If we don't do this or we make a wacky guess (meaning we don't pay attention to the clues), we can create a problem. For example, say you're playing a game in a group and a boy wants you to play the game, but you THINK he is being bossy and you start yelling at him. What might happen?

Let's think more about BOSSY WORDS and TONE OF VOICE. HOW DO YOU KNOW WHEN SOMEONE REALLY IS BEING BOSSY? Or MEAN? Let's practice and see if we can solve this problem below.

Look at how these four clues add up.

How does his or her voice sound (mean or friendly)?

_____

+ What is he or she saying to you? What words is he using?

_____

+ What message is his or her body sending?

_____

+ What do you know about him or her?

_____

= What do you think his or her plan is? (Friendly? Mean?)

_____

Observing Others

We're working on thinking about people and figuring out what their plans are. To get really good at this, we need to practice. One of the *first* steps for figuring out what others are doing (and going to do next) is to watch them. To do this, today we'll go on a people hunt around the school and perhaps into the front office. See how many points you can get by finding people on this list. You can get bonus points for doing things that will show them that you're thinking about them.

GOOD LUCK HUNTERS!

	Did you get any points? (Put them here)	Points
Find someone doing an expected behavior.		2
Bonus: What is the person doing?		10
Find someone doing an unexpected behavior.		2
Bonus: What is the person doing?		10
Find someone working.		2
Bonus: What is the person doing?		10
Find someone who is happy.		2
Bonus: Why do you think the person is happy?		5
Find someone who is concentrating.		2
Bonus: What do you think the person is thinking about? How can you tell?		15
Total Points	Yours	Out of 60

© 2011 Think Social Publishing, Inc. • www.socialthinking.com

Do Video Game Characters Have to Be Social Thinkers?

We use our Social Thinking whenever we have to think about ourselves or others. Thinking about people has to do with Social Thinking!

Social Thinking not only involves hanging out with others but understanding, history, math, English, getting along in P.E. or in other groups, and more.

Do video game characters have to be social thinkers? *Let's explore* and see how they may have to consider others in the game to win.

What is the name of the game?_____

What type of game is it?_____

What is one character's name?_____

Circle the ones below that involve Social Thinking.

Does the character?

Ride or drive any vehicles   Move around other characters

Have to stay focused   Say things to appear cool

Report to any other characters   Congratulate another character

Play any sports   Anticipate the next move

Build or create structures   Know who's a friend or an enemy

Argue with anyone   Say things to keep people calm, cool, and collected

Talk with others to solve a problem

. . . .

How many did you circle that have to do with Social Thinking?

Chapter 3:
Problem Solving

Hidden Rules

Every situation that we're in has hidden rules. Hidden rules are ones that no one really teaches you directly (until now). They are the rules that everyone is just expected to know. Some hidden rules are more obvious like "don't pick your nose in public," but others require a little detective work to see and understand.

For example, one hidden rule is that when someone asks us, "What do you think of my new _____

_____? ," we're supposed to say we like it even if we really don't. Most people know that saying that they don't like the new thing will hurt the person's feelings, and we don't want to do that.

Next, we'll think of other hidden rules for different situations.

What are some hidden rules for coming into your classroom in the morning?

What are some hidden rules for when the teacher is teaching the whole class?

What are some hidden rules for working on a group project with other kids?

What are some hidden rules for eating lunch with other people?

There are so many different sets of hidden rules, with a different set for every situation. There are hidden rules in our homes, in the community, at school, riding our bikes, playing computer games, etc. Why do hidden rules matter? These rules provide a list of what are considered "expected" behaviors in a situation. When someone shares space with other people and does what's expected, others tend to feel good about that person's behavior, and this makes people feel good about the entire person. When someone doesn't necessarily follow the hidden rules, that person is doing what's "unexpected" for the situation. This makes people have uncomfortable thoughts that lead to uncomfortable or negative emotions about that person's behavior. When someone does a lot of unexpected behaviors, it makes some people feel like they don't want to be with that person because that person isn't making them feel good.

Hidden rules are important to sleuth out!

Can you figure out the hidden rules *(the expected set of behaviors)* for the following situations?

1. **Getting ready for school:**

2. **Eating dinner with your family:**

3. **Asking for help in the classroom:**

4. **Getting ready for bed:**

Keep thinking about the hidden rules because they exist in every situation in which people share space together!

Hidden Rules at School

"*Social expectations*" refers to how well you share your space with others at that particular time or place. "*Sharing space*" means that because you're near other people, people are thinking about each other and are supposed to help keep each other calm and focused on whatever it is they are doing. Whenever a situation changes in the world around us, the social expectations change as well. Most people don't talk about these changes in social expectations; it's simply expected that people notice the changes and adjust their behavior to them. Because the expectations aren't usually discussed out loud, we call them the "*hidden social rules.*"

Being *social* does not necessarily mean you're having fun with the people around you. It only means that people are having reasonably "*expected*" or "*normal*" thoughts about you, and you're having these same types of thoughts about them—all based on each others' behaviors, actions, and reactions within a specific situation. To help you explore this, look at the following example and then fill out the next two rows on your own. If you don't have experience with one of these situations, cross it out and write in one with which you're more familiar!

Complete the following:

The situation	What are the social expectations/hidden rules that go along with that setting?	What do you have to do to adjust your own behavior to the expectations? Why should you do this?
Getting ready for bed	Avoid complaining—it's just part of the routine of the day. Change into pajamas. Brush your teeth. Say goodnight to your parents. Get in bed. Read or turn off the light. *(These will depend on your specific situation.)*	Transition away from whatever you were doing without complaining. Move through these different, familiar steps independently. Make sure you say goodnight to your parent(s) or whatever adult you live with. *Why? It allows you to get some rest and keeps other people in your house feeling good when they don't have to nag you. They're tired at the end of a day too!!*
Eating lunch at school		Describe the situation Why should you do this?

The situation	What are the social expectations/hidden rules that go along with that setting?	What do you have to do to adjust your own behavior to the expectations? Why should you do this?
Turning in your homework		Describe the situation Why should you do this?

© 2011 Think Social Publishing, Inc. • www.socialthinking.com

Hidden Rules in the Classroom

The hidden rules in the classroom are those that all students in the school are expected to know but are ones that haven't been directly taught. The hidden rules include little things related to others' thoughts about us such as how to dress, how to act, what to do, and what not to do. They also include when to talk to someone, with whom to talk, what people to ignore, and so on. It also includes knowing 1) teachers' specific social expectations, 2) teacher-pleasing behaviors, 3) students who treat you well, 4) individuals who are likely to get you in trouble, 5) behaviors that attract positive attention from teachers and peers, and 6) behaviors that are considered negative or inappropriate (*unexpected*) by teachers and peers. (Myles, Trautman, and Schelvan, ***The Hidden Curriculum***, 2004).

Because these hidden rules are not discussed out loud, we all have to be social spies to try and figure out the social expectations around us. Think about the following questions, and then take some time to be a spy as you determine what the answers are for your particular situation!

. . . .

1. How can you tell when one of your teachers is upset with someone in the class because the teacher doesn't usually say, "I am upset with_____"! What exactly does the teacher do that lets you know how he or she is thinking and feeling?

2. How does one of your teachers show you that he or she is happy with your performance?

3. How does one of your teachers communicate that he or she is frustrated with you in particular?

4. Can you joke with all your teachers or with just some of them? Which ones? How do you know?

5. Can you joke with them at any time, or are there specific times when you can joke with them? How do you know when it's okay to joke with them and when it's not?

6. Choose one of your teachers and figure out what you think this teacher thinks is the MOST important thing for the students to do in this class. Feel free to ask the teacher directly to help you figure this out. If you found out the information by observation, how did you figure it out?

7. Thinking about this same teacher, what are the things one or many students do that seem to make the teacher frustrated the fastest?

8. What are the rules in this class about talking to other students during class time? How did you figure this out?

9. How flexible is this teacher about turning in homework late?

10. Why is turning in homework important to this teacher?

11. Do you think this teacher likes you? If so, how does he or she demonstrate that to you and others?

For more information about this concept, see Myles, Trautman, and Schelvan, **The Hidden Curriculum***, 2004.*

Hidden Rules for Middle School

Social rules and laws are everywhere. What are they at your school?

....

1. People act differently in different situations. Sometimes people treat you differently when they're around certain other people.
   - What does this mean? Why do people do this? Do you do this?

2. Once you're in middle school, it's not cool to hug or kiss your parents around friends. You can hug them when it's just your family at home or if you're leaving for a trip.
   - Why have the rules changed as you have gotten older? *(Tip: Think about what other kids are thinking to answer this.)*

3. Other people's impressions of you and the impressions you have of other people are always changing.
   - How have you changed what you think and feel about another student or teacher in your school?

4. Even if you know you're right, arguing with your parents sometimes gets you into more trouble than if you said nothing.
   - Why is this? *(Tip: Think about it from a parent's point of view.)*

5. It is not always okay to point out specific things about a person's personal appearance or clothing; it may make them feel uncomfortable.
   - Why is this?

6. By middle school, jokes that you tell friends are usually different from jokes that you tell adults.
   - Why is this? Can you give an example?

7. Humor is tricky. A joke is not always funny—whether it's funny or not depends on whether it's told at the right time, in the right place, and with the right people.
   - Can you give an example of a time you noticed a student using humor at the wrong time, in the wrong place, or with the wrong person?

8. If you do something funny, it's usually only funny once. If you do it repeatedly, it makes you look goofy and may annoy people if you continue to say the same joke over and over again.
   - Why is this; can you explain?

9. When someone talks to you or if you listen to someone talk in a group, it's important that you show the person you're being a good listener even if you're doing the social fake (making eye contact, turning your body toward the person, keeping your brain connected to the person's thoughts and words, adding relevant thoughts to the topic).
   - Why is it important to act like you are listening to someone? (*Tip: Think about it from your own perspective; how do you expect people to treat you when you are talking?*)

10. There are certain questions you do not ask others because they're considered personal questions. These questions may include finding out about someone's weight, grades, scores on tests, age (if it's an adult), income, religion, and politics.
    - Why are some questions more personal than others? (*Tip: Think about it from your own point of view and then the point of view of others. Do you think you share the same point of view on this?*)

11. If someone intrudes into your space, politely ask the person to move over without touching him or her.
    - When you were young, it was okay to touch someone else. Why isn't it okay now that you're older?

12. When someone asks, "How do you like my new _____? ," the person usually really wants you to say you like it. Even if you don't like it, try to find something positive to say.
    - Even though your answer may not be totally honest, why is it important that you not always tell the literal truth? (*Tip: Think about this from the point of view of how someone feels based on what is said to him or her.*)

13. When you leave a situation or place where you've been talking to others in the group, always say goodbye.
    - Why?

14. Correcting other people during a conversation can be annoying to the group or person you are talking with. Sometimes people make mistakes and it is not always best to tell them when they make mistakes.
    - Why shouldn't you correct people in social situations?

15. When working with a group of students in a classroom, a teacher may correct a student's answer if the teacher thinks it needs improvement.
    - Why isn't it okay for a student to correct another student's answer in front of the whole classroom or even in a small group? (*Tip: Think about how what we say affects how people feel.*)

Adapted from Myles, Trautman, and Shelvan, *The Hidden Curriculum*, 2004.

What Is Blurting?

Blurting is anything you do with your words or your body that interrupts the thoughts of another person in an unexpected way. Blurting is considered a rude behavior because it doesn't show you thought about others when you added your words or body to the group.

What type of *impression* does it make if you blurt with your words in class or shove your way into a group?

When you BLURT with your words, it means:

- You aren't really paying attention to what the other person is saying. Others will interpret this to mean that you think what you have to say is more important than what someone else has to say.

- You aren't paying attention to who the speaker is thinking about when she is talking; you weren't thinking with your eyes.

- You make comments out loud while the teacher is talking, even though the other kids are keeping those same thoughts inside their heads.

When you BLURT with your body, it means:

- You make big body movements that distract other people.

- You unexpectedly walk into a group or away from the group, distracting other people's thoughts. For example, if you enter a group that is working together in a way that all the attention is drawn to you so people can't concentrate on what they were doing or saying, you have "barged into" the group. This is the physical form of blurting.

- You touch another person in an unexpected way.

To avoid blurting:

a. Think with your eyes. If someone is looking at another person (that is, thinking about this other person) while they're talking, it is probably not expected that you start talking at that moment.

b. Enter slowly, subtly, and quietly into a group so that as you enter, you tend to blend into the group rather than call all the attention to yourself.

Blurting

Being in a group can be especially challenging when it comes to sharing the time with others. When we're in a group our job is to share our ideas as well as to listen to what others say. We also need to look interested even if the topic isn't too exciting to us. One concept that can affect the *flow* of a group is called BLURTING.

Blurting is when we DO or SAY something that interrupts the group's thoughts and the overall *flow* of what is happening.

What might others think if you blurt?

Can you list three ways you can blurt with your words or ways you've seen others do a word blurt?

1.

2.

3.

Do you blurt with your words? *(Circle one)*

Never   Sometimes   Often

Can you list three ways you've seen others or yourself blurt with their bodies?

1.

2.

3.

Social Thinking® Thinksheets for Tweens and Teens

Body Messages! Are You Confusing Others?

Our bodies include our face, arms, hands, legs, posture, and so on. Our bodies can do all kinds of things for us. Many times we can use our bodies to communicate a message without even using our words. For example, if you ask someone a question and she responds by shrugging her shoulders, she may have communicated that she doesn't know the answer. The body does things that people observe and then try to interpret. For example, people try and interpret how we feel based on how we look (for example, if our facial expression looks sad, people think we are sad).

People might also try and guess what we're thinking about based on what we're doing (for example, if we pull out a cell phone and start playing a game on it during class, people think we're not paying attention to the teacher). People look at us when we're near them and try to interpret what we're thinking, doing, feeling, etc. You should try and do this too when you sit in a class, walk down a hall, or at lunch break.

You'll find that it's not always clear what people are thinking, feeling, or planning. Sometimes we confuse others because our bodies may do something that's unexpected, and this may make people have weird or uncomfortable thoughts about us. When we're around others, we don't just monitor what we say to each other, we also try and control how our bodies appear to them to try and help control what people think about us.

What might happen if you tell your body to appear *in a way that's different from others* or to *do* something that's *unexpected in the situation*?

How do you feel when others give unexpected body messages?

List some things someone's body can do that can make that person stand out or look different from the group.

In the classroom:

1.   2.

In a school assembly:

1.   2.

At lunch:

1.   2.

While others talk to that person:

1.   2.

Can you think of one **good message** YOUR BODY sends to others during the school day?

Can you think of one **confusing message** YOUR BODY sends to others during the school day?

Discuss with a parent or teacher one thing you can learn to better observe how your body is being perceived by others. Try and monitor how others use their bodies in this way.

Try and observe how others perceive you based on what you're doing with your body.

Report back to your parent or teacher about this!

Social Thinking® Thinksheets for Tweens and Teens   © 2011 Think Social Publishing, Inc. • www.socialthinking.com

Correcting Other Students When You're a Black-and-White Thinker

People's brains work in *different* ways. Some people think in very exact ways. We call this "thinking in black and white" because people who think like this see things as either one way or another. These black-and-white thinkers like to learn facts and can memorize details easily. They tend to like things to be perfect. They don't like mistakes and will correct others frequently.

Some people think more about the possible options rather than see things as happening one way or another. They see things in between black and white *(in shades of gray)*. In other words, they tend to learn whole concepts *(shades of gray)* rather than focus on details or seeing situations as one way or another *(black and white)*. Surgeons need to be exact and focus on details. Gray thinkers, such as teachers, think in more general terms and see a bigger picture while helping students to also focus on specific facts.

People who are black-and-white thinkers tend to get more frustrated in school than gray-area thinkers. This is because when black-and-white thinkers think about how they do their schoolwork, they see it as either doing it wrong or doing it right. When they do their work correctly (right), they're satisfied, but doing it wrong can make them very sad, frustrated, and even angry. They don't like to make mistakes, and they often don't like to correct mistakes once they're made.

Black-and-white thinkers also tend to notice when others make mistakes as well. When they notice that someone spelled a word incorrectly or isn't following a rule correctly, they can become frustrated. They want to insist that people follow all the rules and know how to write words correctly.

Often black-and-white thinkers tell others that they made a mistake and then tell them how to fix it. As logical as this sounds, this type of correction can be very frustrating to gray-area thinkers. Such thinkers believe that rules are not to be followed exactly. They think that the most important thing isn't getting the work done perfectly, but is instead feeling okay when they work around others. When another student tells them they're doing something wrong, they get embarrassed, meaning that they worry people are having weird or uncomfortable thoughts about them. This can also make them feel frustrated or even mad at the person who told them they did their work wrong! Gray-area thinkers believe that teachers are the ones in the classroom who should point out if a student does something incorrectly. If a student wants help from another student, the student will ask the other student directly. *For example*, the gray-area thinking student may say to another student, "Do you know how to spell this word?" Once a student asks another student for help, help can be offered and will be accepted well.

Whether we're a black-and-white thinker or a gray-area thinking student or a teacher, everyone at some point will make not one but many mistakes. When students learn as part of a group, students need to know that other students don't like their mistakes to be corrected by peers. If a black-and-white thinker has his or her brain get stuck on another student's mistake, that person can write down the correct answer in a blurting journal.

What's a blurting journal? It's a small notebook that people can use to quietly write down the thoughts they have to get them out of their brain. Writing down these thoughts in the journal also keeps the black-and-white thinker from announcing the thoughts in class, which may make one or many students and even the teacher feel bad.

What to Do When a Teacher Makes a Mistake

Surprisingly, even teachers make mistakes. Teachers also have feelings about the students in their class and how the students treat the teacher when things are going well and when things aren't going so well in class.

Telling a teacher she is wrong in front of the class is often considered a rude thing to do because it embarrasses the teacher and possibly the other students who are listening.

What we say to people affects how they feel about you. A teacher still has a lot of feelings. If a student tells the teacher that the teacher is teaching the incorrect information, the teacher will probably feel many negative emotions.

For example, the teacher might write on the board that the spelling test is on Thursday, but you know that the test is always on Friday. If you then say to the teacher, "You're wrong. The spelling test is on Friday!", your information may be accurate but the way you spoke to the teacher in front of the class is considered rude or insulting. This may make the teacher upset with you because you didn't think about how you made her feel.

There are more *subtle* ways to let a teacher know you're not sure if what he or she is teaching is correct. One way to do this is to tell the teacher that you're confused.

If you say you're confused, you don't directly say the teacher is doing it wrong, so you don't directly make him feel bad. By saying, "I'm confused," you let the teacher know that something she did or said doesn't let your brain figure out what you need to learn.

Teachers are there to help. It's their job to help you be less confused. If you tell the teacher, "I'm confused about which day the spelling test is on, Thursday or Friday," the teacher is likely to realize she made a mistake all on her own. While she still may feel a little embarrassed, it's not nearly as bad as if you announced it to the whole class.

. . . .

To summarize:

What we say to people, including teachers, affects how they feel about themselves and about you, the person who said it. As you grow up, you have to learn to choose your words more carefully. Choose to say words that help people to learn that they may have said something that confused you, without making it seem like they just keep making mistakes!

When Is It Okay to Correct Other Kids?

Sometimes you feel like you just have to tell someone what to do or how to do something!

But—this means other people may think you're being bossy.

Bossy—A bossy person is defined as a person who frequently tells other people what to do.

People don't usually like to talk to or hang out with a *bossy* person, because by telling you what to do he acts like you can't think for yourself. People also start to think that the *bossy* person doesn't care about how others think or feel. They think he just wants things to turn out his way.

When people hang out or talk to each other, a hidden rule is that all people want to feel like their thoughts count too! If people feel like others are appreciating what they have to say, they tend to feel good about being with those people.

People often avoid hanging out with a *bossy* person because the *bossy* person doesn't make others feel good about themselves.

. . . .

When is it okay to tell others to stop doing something or to make a comment about their behavior?

1. When they are physically or verbally hurting another person!

2. When they are doing mean teasing!

3. When they just won't stop doing something that you don't like, even after an adult or other kids have told them over and over to stop (*for example, tickling*)!

4. When someone else does something that's so irritating to you that you might explode with anger or frustration! (It's better to ask someone to stop doing a behavior rather than to get really mad.)

Steps to Solving a Problem

1. Identify the problem.

What is the problem?

Is it a big problem, a medium problem, or a small problem?

How can you help to make this problem smaller or to help it go away completely?

Self-Talk: Okay, I have a problem and it is _____.

I need to stay calm and _____ .

2. Think of solutions.

You need to listen to the person trying to help you to see if he or she has ideas for good choices you can make to help solve your problem.

You have choices that may help you to "solve" the problem. When we say we're "problem solving," what we really mean is that we're doing something to make the problem smaller. We may not actually make it completely go away!

An example is if you refuse to do your homework, but then you finally decide to get it done though you turn it in late. You may not get as much credit for it, but it was a far better choice than not doing it at all. So you made the problem smaller. We call that "problem solving."

List two good choices that would help to make your problem smaller:

1.

2.

Self-Talk: Okay, I have some choices that could be solutions. By staying calm I can focus on which would be the better choice or if I should use both of them. Sometimes we use several choices to solve one problem.

3. Think about the consequences and put a plan in motion!
We're always looking a bit into the future when we problem solve. We try and figure out what we want to happen if we choose one choice or another choice. Figuring out what will happen next based on a choice we make is called determining the "consequences." We usually like consequences that make a situation less stressful, make ourselves and others calmer, and/or help us get done what we need to do!

For each of your choices above, write out a consequence that will happen if you use that choice:

Consequence for Choice 1:_____

Consequence for Choice 2:_____

4. Choose your choice(s) and make a plan.

a. Select which choice or choices will help you reach the result you want. Now, make a plan to put your choice into action. This means you will have to take action. Use the questions below to help you figure out how and when to do what needs to be done:

b. Getting going with choices:

1. When will you do it?

2. What do you need to say or do?

3. To whom do you need to say it? (Skip this step if there's nothing to say!)

4. Where do you need to do it?

5. When do you need to do it?

6. How will you reward yourself for getting it done? (Sometimes our rewards are simply telling ourselves we did a good job and reminding ourselves that we're getting better at solving our problems! Rewards aren't always about getting something we want. Eliminating stress can be a huge reward!!)

5. Evaluate the outcome.

Did the solution work? Why or why not?

What could you have done differently?

How can you avoid a similar problem in the future?

*Oh yeah, and by the way, **CONGRATULATIONS!***

Emotion and Behavior Thermometer

Emotions		Level of problem associated with emotion	Behavior that would make sense given the level of the problem:
Very upset Highly anxious or nervous Freaked out		Emergency	Screaming, being frantic, yelling *It's almost impossible to be a flexible thinker!*
Depressed Nervous Worried Sad		Problematic!	Upset face, tense body, unhappy words *You have to work harder at being a flexible thinker, but you can still do it when you feel this way!*
A bit nervous Excited Calm Relaxed Happy		I'm Fine!	Flexible thinking Relaxed, calm, happy face, friendly words, flexible brain, doing the social fake!

Social Thinking® Thinksheets for Tweens and Teens

Problem Solving Scale

Instructions:
Draw a line between a problem, the size reaction you think corresponds to the problem and the related emotion. Discuss your responses with your teacher and peers. Do people agree with the size of your reactions to the different problems?

Are you a person who tends to have bigger reactions than others would have? Are you a person that has smaller reactions to problems than is expected? The more you learn about yourself the more you learn how to get along with others even during problem times.

Different types of problems	Reaction	Emotion/Feeling
Stranger attacking me	Big	Scared
EARTHQUAKE		Angry
Medical emergency		
Being bullied		
Dog bite	Medium	Worried/Anxious
Fighting at school		Frustrated
Forgot homework more than once		
Missed several days of school		
Being teased		
Schedule change	Tiny/No Problem!	Calm
Someone won't share		
Lose a game		
Fly in my face—ignore it, shoo it away		
Shoe unties		
A group task I don't like to do		

OOPS...I Messed Up and Now I Better Think About It!

Describe what happened that caused this problem.(Because people are mad at me, this is, at least in part, my problem.)

_____

When I got into this situation, I got angry. I looked angry, I said angry words, etc. How did my actions make other people feel? Do they remember those feelings?

_____

_____

For every problem there is more than one solution. Below I need to write at least three solutions to the problem, including the bad solution, which is probably the one I already chose!

1. (Bad solution)_____

2. (A good solution I should have tried)_____

3. (Another good solution I should have tried)_____

If I had tried the good solutions, they would have led to a different set of consequences. That means had I done things differently, they could have turned out differently. I probably would not have such a big problem. Had I used one of the above good choices, I think things would have ended up making my problem smaller: *(describe)*

_____

_____

The good news is we all make mistakes, which means we get to practice fixing our mistakes. People often start to do this with flexible thinking, which means figuring out how to apologize and then how to show the people that got upset by my actions that I'm trying to make better choices when I'm with them.

When I apologize, I will say:

_____

_____

And then I will show I'm sorry by saying or doing the following things:

_____

When I have done something wrong, it's very normal to feel bad for a little bit. That is OKAY! That means I'm AWARE and SORRY FOR WHAT I HAVE DONE and will try not to do it in the future! If we do get better and are not as likely to have this problem again, we call that "learning from our mistakes."

The Winner

A WINNER :

Someone who other people enjoy playing with and want to play with again!

How to be a winner *(even if you come in last):*

Be a good sport

Use friendly words and tone of voice

Make supportive comments

Play fair

Congratulate others (no bragging)

Take turns

Pay attention to the game

NOT A WINNER :

Someone who other people don't enjoy playing with and don't want to play with again!

What NOT to do:

Be a bad sport

Be bossy or try to control the situation

Use mean or unfriendly words or tone of voice

Brag about winning or being in first place

Not follow the rules

Be inflexible (having a "Rock Brain")

Make fun of someone

Not pay attention

Cheat

Social Thinking® Thinksheets for Tweens and Teens

Survival Guide to Middle School!

Middle school can be a hectic time for anyone! There are so many new hidden rules and expected behaviors. So, in order to *survive* let's make a guide to help others as well as us navigate this confusing territory.

What parts do we need to include in our guide?

-
-
-

-
-
-

What topics should we include in our guide?

-
-
-

-
-
-

What topic or part of the guide would I like to focus on, and how can I contribute to the guide?

-
-
-

-
-
-

What is my homework? What should I bring to contribute to the guide?

-
-
-

-
-
-

Social Thinking in and around the Classroom

Think about the following situations. Describe how these situations end up.

. . . .

1. A teacher says, "You must do your homework," and you don't know to whom she is talking. What should you say or do?

2. You're frustrated in a class so you just shut down and you don't say anything. What are other people thinking, that is, teachers and students?

3. You are frustrated in a class so you say that you don't care and that this is stupid. What are other people thinking, that is, teachers and students?

4. Other kids are talking all around you before the class starts. What should you say or do? How will people receive your behavior?

5. The teacher has started the class and kids are talking. What should you say or do? How will people receive your behavior?

6. You raise your hand to answer a question, and you tell the teacher much more than she asked for. What will people think about your behavior?

7. A teacher mispronounces a word, but everyone knows what she is talking about. What do you do?

8. A student causes trouble in class and you don't like him. This kid is sticking gum on the floor, on purpose. What do you do?

9. Your teacher says, "Turn in your homework" to the whole class, and you say out loud, "I already did. In fact, I turned it in early." How will people see your behavior?

10. Kids are having a conversation and you jump into it and add your thoughts even though they are not talking to you. What will kids think?

11. A kid is telling some folks how he feels and you tell him that he should not feel that way. How will your behavior be received?

12. The classroom is noisy. What should you do?

13. A student is defending her absences to her teacher. You overhear and think the girl is lying. What do you do?

14. A friend says "Hi" to you when you were not expecting to see her. What do you do? Why?

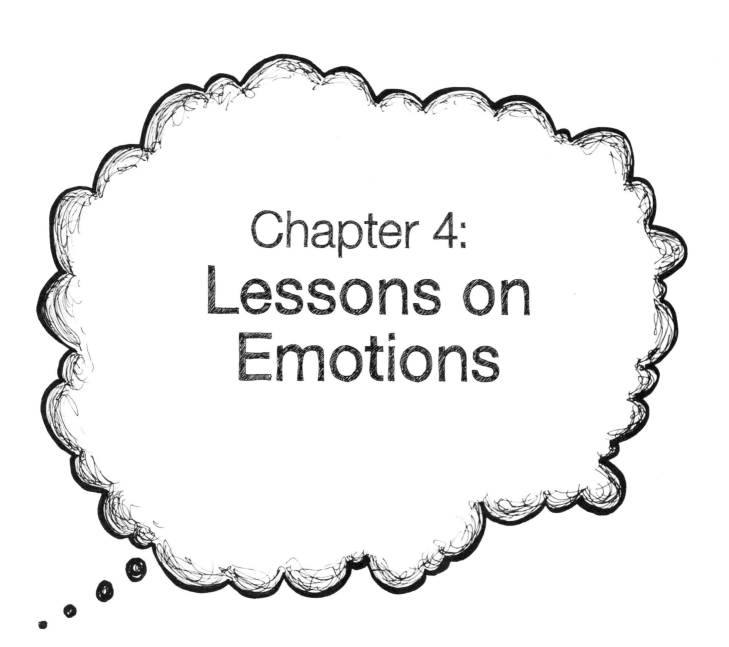

Chapter 4:
Lessons on
Emotions

How Do You FEEL and How Does It Change My Feelings?

How we feel on the inside changes how we act on the outside!
How we act on the outside changes what people THINK and FEEL about us.

CALM	WORRIED OR A LITTLE MAD	STRESSED OR VERY MAD
What do my body and face look like?	What do my body and face look like?	What do my body and face look like?
What does my voice sound like?	What does my voice sound like?	What does my voice sound like?
What type of words do I say?	What type of words do I say?	What type of words do I say?
How do I make people feel?	How do I make people feel?	How do I make people feel?
What do they think about me?	What do they think about me?	What do they think about me?

People often remember how other people made them feel. How will people remember you when you're calm and friendly? How will they remember you when you're VERY MAD?

_____

_____

_____

Most of us want to be remembered as friendly. We use our flexible thinking to remind us what we can do to try and help keep ourselves calm. What kind of things do you remind yourself to do when you want to stay calm by using your flexible thinking?

_____

_____

_____

What are some things you can do at school to help you improve how you work with other kids?

_____

_____

_____

What are some things you can do at home to try and help you hang out in a better way with a brother, sister, or another relative?

_____

_____

_____

Positive or Negative: Which Do You Want to Be?

If you are being POSITIVE:

You will look, feel, sound, and act happy.

You will have a happy or neutral face.

You will use happy and kind words.

You will give compliments.

You will have a flexible brain.

People will have good thoughts about you and will want to keep being around you.

When we're in a group or around others, we have to find a way to be positive. If we can't, we are not being part of the group and must go away from the group because it makes the group feel uncomfortable.

. . . .

If you are being NEGATIVE:

You will look, feel, sound, and act negative.

You will look unhappy, mad, or have a sour face.

You will probably use mean or unkind words.

You might even insult people.

You definitely will have a Rock Brain.

If you are being negative and are being part of the group, you will have to go outside the room.

People will have uncomfortable thoughts about you.

People will feel uncomfortable around you and will not want to spend much time with you.

People might avoid you in the future and might say, "He's always grumpy. I don't want to be around him."

Optimist or Pessimist: Which One Are You?

An *optimist* is someone who thinks the best possible outcome of actions or events will happen.

A *pessimist* is someone who thinks that the worst possible outcome of actions or events will happen.

An *optimistic* person believes and finds positive solutions or reasons for things that happen. For example, if someone bumps into him, an optimist will imagine or reason the best-case scenario (that it was an accident). A *pessimistic* person will imagine or reason the worst-case scenario (that the person bumped into her on purpose and is out to get her).

How do you think the *optimist* feels about other people in general? Do you think the *optimist* generally likes others or is skeptical about them?

How do you think the *pessimist* feels about other people in general? Do you think the *pessimist* generally likes others or is skeptical about them?

Write an **O = Optimist** or a **P = Pessimist** to describe each of the characteristics below:

_____Thinks positively about others

_____Trusts others

_____Feels bad about himself

_____Thinks negatively about others

_____Gives others the benefit of the doubt

_____Thinks others are out to get her

_____Feels good about the world and feels good about himself

_____Thinks others are lying or have some kind of ulterior motive

Pessimistic people aren't very pleasant to be around. They often complain about others or the world around them, and that kind of attitude brings down others too. When we're around *optimistic* people, we feel good, and we want to be around them more. They feel positive, think positively, and make positive remarks, and that's fun to be around!

See how many optimists you can find!!

Big Packages or Small Packages?

Every day people try to figure out things about each other. *For example*, we try to figure out what other people are thinking, how they're feeling, and if they're people we want to be with.

We all are expected to observe the body, eyes, and words used by others while also trying to figure out what they're thinking. Other people do the same thing with us—they try and figure us out. If you act in a way that makes people have strong, usually negative, thoughts about you, you are sending the message in a BIG PACKAGE.

We have to be very careful about how we send a message to someone. We may feel really frustrated and want to send someone a BIG MESSAGE: stomping our feet, growling, crossing our arms, and making an angry face. But it may not be the right time to send such a BIG PACKAGE. Other people don't always like to get big packages and may not want to be around you if you always send BIG PACKAGES. BIG PACKAGES usually make other people uncomfortable. And when they're uncomfortable, they also may not be very helpful or friendly.

By the time we're 10 years old, we're supposed to be able to send messages in smaller packages, even when we're upset. A small package means people don't see us being so mad. It definitely takes practice to learn to send smaller package messages.

When you send a smaller package message, people may know that you're irritated with the situation (because you may look a little frustrated, you may say, "this is not easy for me," and you may use a tone of voice that does not sound like you're happy).

However, you don't look like you're about to get really mad at the person near you. To send a small package, we may still feel upset but we don't let people see us looking so mad. Instead, we can think mad thoughts, but we help to control how angry we look to other people.

We do this by thinking about how our Big Package reaction will make others treat us badly in return. We think about controlling how we show our feelings by trying to take a deep breath, to keep our bodies a little calmer, and to avoid saying things that will feed other people jerk food!

Sending a Message
Small Messages and Big Messages

As you get into middle school and high school, you have to think about how to send your messages to someone in a small package. This means when we feel a certain way about something or someone, we need to express this feeling in a way that is not so obvious. People are expected to infer or predict what someone is thinking based on little things they do.

If we choose to send a BIG MESSAGE such as yelling, screaming, and throwing things at someone when we're mad at them, we will stand out and look weird or look like the "bad" guy or girl. So it's important to think about how to send a small message when we feel a certain way. We sometimes can send a clear message with our body language (for example, turning our bodies away from someone we're mad at or ignoring them and walking past them).

If you can learn to send small messages like many of your classmates have learned to do, this will help you fit in and look more like the kids around you. Ultimately, if you learn to send smaller messages to others, they may respond more positively to you in general!

- -

How can you send a message that you're mad?

Small message

BIG MESSAGE

How can you send a message that you like someone or have a crush on them?

Small message

BIG MESSAGE

. . . .

When excited describe how you could send small messages with your body, face, and words and how you would use your body, face, eyes, language, and/or voice to send a big message:

Small message

BIG MESSAGE

Small Messages

When people bother us, it's important to send small but clear messages to them to get them to stop. If we send a BIG message, we'll attract attention to ourselves and may end up getting in trouble.

Let's think of some small messages we can send to get others to stop bothering us!

1._____

_____

2._____

_____

3._____

_____

When someone is bothering us, we *feel*_____

_____

When we react in a BIG way, how do other people feel about us?

_____

_____

_____

When we react in a small and expected way, how do people feel about us? How do they remember us *(positive or negative memory)*?

_____

_____

_____

Ignoring: Sending a Small but Powerful Message

When we're frustrated or upset with someone, there are ways that we're EXPECTED TO DEAL WITH THIS! This is just a rule of LIFE! One way that we can send the message that we don't like someone is by simply ignoring the person. By doing this, you're sending the message (in a small package that will not draw bad attention to you) that you don't want to be around the person and you do not care for him or her. Let's look at how we can ignore someone to send the message that we don't like the person.

How do you ignore with your eyes?

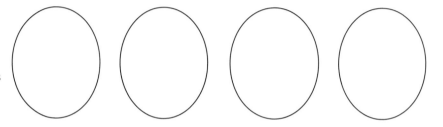

If a person is standing right in front of you, draw two directions your eyes might LOOK to ignore that person.

Staring at a person is NOT a way to ignore them! STARING at the person while also looking unhappy sends a big package message that you are upset at a person. *For example: When a teacher stares at a student with a serious look on her face, it usually means she is scolding the student.*

How do you ignore with your head? *Typically we do this by turning not only our eyes away from the person we are ignoring, but our entire head turns away from him or her as well. In fact, you may just want to completely walk away from a person you are ignoring.*

How do you ignore with your whole body? *Remember, small messages = small movements!*

Draw a body that is ignoring.

Let's look at what a small package looks like compared to a BIG PACKAGE.

You don't win a game that you're playing with your friends:

BIG Package	Small Package
Brain:	Brain:
Body:	Body:
Eyes:	Eyes:
Words:	Words:

Every month and every year, you get a little bit older. As we grow up, it is expected that we can better control ourselves when we feel upset so we don't frighten or intimidate others. This is a VERY IMPORTANT set of skills to learn. We all still feel very upset or frustrated; we just learn a more effective way to communicate about our problem so people are still willing to help us solve it. We all need people to help us work through life's hard problems, even as adults. It is not bad to feel upset; it is learning how to stay calm even when things are upsetting that is important for your own success! At your age, one of the ways people talk about this is by calling it a "big package message" or a "small package message." You may also hear others refer to "self-control" or "self-regulation" when you have control and are using a small package message. Being "dysregulated" is another way to describe a "big package message."

If you like learning new terms, when you become a young adult, the ability to control how you react to a big problem or upset is called using "emotional compression." One of the things about language is that you will hear adults use many different terms for talking about the same thing! How we describe our emotional control also changes with age!

Persistence and Embarrassment

By middle school most kids are strongly aware of being embarrassed by others or doing things that would embarrass themselves. Teenagers feel embarrassed by things that usually would not embarrass adults. For example, teenagers get embarrassed really easily by their family (parents, brothers, sisters, and other relatives).

Embarrassment is defined as a feeling of self-consciousness, shame, or awkwardness, such as the feeling you have when you know that another person is having a bad or weird thought about you.

At times, teenagers persist through games or activities they don't enjoy just so they don't get people to have weird or bad thoughts about them.

A weird thought is when people think about the fact that you're doing some behaviors in a place where they're unexpected. *For example*, arguing with a teacher in class or refusing to do work can make people have a weird thought about you because it is unexpected.

You have weird or bad thoughts about others sometimes. *Think* about when you have these thoughts in these different places:

Home—

School—

Store or Restaurant—

Now think of other people in your family or your friends.

When do they have weird or uncomfortable thoughts about others—*at home, at, school, in a store, a restaurant, or a movie theater?*

When do you have "weird" or "uncomfortable" thoughts about them?

Persist Through Challenges

One of the things you can work on is helping yourself to persist and get through times that may be CHALLENGING, BORING, or FRUSTRATING. Sometimes the challenges can be small or quite large. This can be a difficult task for anyone and can affect us daily. List some activities or situations that could be negatively affected if we do not persist and appropriately get through them.

1.

2.

How would this make you feel in the end? How might others feel around you if you have a hard time persisting through challenges?

Let's take a look at how you (your brain) respond when you're presented with a challenge.

	How do your body and/or words react to this situation?	How are others affected? (How might they feel?)
You're given a challenging writing assignment.		
Your parents need you to get off the computer.		
You have to work with someone you don't like very much.		
You have to go with your mom on an errand.		
You have to do 25 math problems for homework.		
Can you think of more situations?		

How will learning to persist through challenges help you?

How does learning to persist at learning relate to being a social thinker?

Persistence Pays Off

Persistence is the ability to work hard at something even when it does not feel good to do it right at that moment!!

In some situations, it's easy to persist. Name some of these:

Why is it easy to persist in these situations?

In some situations, it's really hard to persist. Name some of these:

Why is it hard to persist in these situations?

What can make it easier?

I Don't Want to, But I Will Anyhow...

Every day we're forced to do things that we just don't want to do or like to do. For example—I hate doing the dishes, but if I don't do the dishes, they pile up in the sink and someone else might have to clean up after me! Somehow these things end up getting done whether we like to or not.

Here is my list of things that I *have* to do regularly that I don't like to do:

- Take out the garbage
- Do the dishes
- Do the laundry
- Make dinner—sometimes I'm just too tired to cook
- Pay bills
- Drive to work
- Get out of bed in the morning
- Go to the grocery store
- Go to the dentist
- Fill up my car with gas

What are some things that you do every day or regularly that you don't like to do but just have to anyway because it is your job or responsibility?

Why do you do these things?

How does it make others feel when you do them without complaining?

How does it make others feel when you don't do them and you complain about them?

Do you end up feeling better about yourself if you end up doing them and getting them done, or not doing them and people are upset with you?

Emotions Can Be Contagious!

Emotions are like germs; you can spread them!

People catch each others' emotions and start to feel them themselves. Have you ever thought about the fact that when you're with happy people, they often start to make you feel happy too? How about when you're with someone who is angry; how does that start to make you feel?

. . . .

Emotions are like germs; they are contagious!

Sometimes they are good germs; emotions that make other people feel happy should be spread all around. Sometimes emotions are the unpleasant germs that spread to make other people feel bad.

. . . .

We cannot easily control which emotions we feel, but we can learn to control how we show them to others!

We have our own ways we feel about something. No one can tell you NOT to feel the way you do, but people can ask you not to show your feelings so clearly...because emotions are like germs and bad germs are not good to spread! As students get older (fourth and fifth grade, middle school, etc.), it is expected that they show their emotions much more carefully. For example, instead of pouting when you're frustrated, you just don't look happy.

. . . .

Sometimes we even hide our feelings...just so that we don't spread around some bad germs.

When you want to be with a group of friends or work together in a classroom, there are times when you are NOT going to like what's happening in the group! You may not get to choose the activity, go first, or win the game... and you can feel frustrated. However, if you want people to still want you in the group, you can't make your frustration contagious.

What would you do to make people THINK you are okay, even if you don't feel happy about what's going on?

Calmly Explaining How I Feel

Why is it important to tell other people how you feel?

Starting about the time we were in third grade, we have been expected to tell a teacher how we feel without strongly showing how we feel, especially when we're upset or really frustrated.

People cannot completely read your mind. If you're doing a good job controlling the size of your emotions so you don't look upset, people may not know that you're confused, feeling bad, etc. Therefore, you use your words to calmly explain to people how you feel. People can help us solve our problem if we're calm while explaining why we feel bad. When we stay calm, it helps others to stay calm. This helps everyone to be a better problem solver, to help change the situation to erase some of the frustration or upset feelings.

. . . .

My Mood Monitor

 "Happy": I feel great. When I feel great, I am more flexible and I can see things from other people's points of view! My face looks calm and is maybe even smiling.

 "Pretty good": I feel pretty good. Things are fine, and I can think about other people's needs as well as my own. I usually look calm but may not be smiling.

 "Okay": I feel okay when I'm not feeling any kind of happiness but I am not feeling any kind of upset or irritation. I just am fine.

 "Irritated" or _"Frustrated"_: I feel a little upset. I don't like something that's going on around me. I may not like how someone treated me or I may not like something I have to do. I am expected to stay calm and use a calm voice and face. I do what I need to do, but I just don't feel great about doing it. Sometimes this is when I need to ask for help, because I'm not really sure what is expected of me.

 "Mad" or _"Furious"_: I feel really upset. My face looks tight (angry), my voice sounds stressed, and I'm not doing what I need to do because I'm really stuck in feeling bad. I can tell a good friend, parent, or teacher why I'm mad, but they may not always be able to "fix" the problem. Sometimes just telling someone how I feel helps to make it not feel so "big"!

Controlling the Size of Our Emotions So Others Want to Be Around Us!

When we get upset, we can tell someone about how we feel, but we still have to learn how to control how we show our emotions. This is called learning to "control our behavior." It doesn't mean you're not still feeling a bit upset, but it does mean you're learning how to control how you show your emotions to others. This is an important part of growing up...because you don't want your emotions to be contagious!

When you learn a way to help yourself change a behavior, you're learning to use a new "strategy" or "tool." Think about the different strategies you can use in the following situations:

When I got mad, I tried to calm myself by:

_____

_____

_____

I solved the problem that caused me to get upset by:

_____

_____

_____

How did people around me feel when I used my strategies to control my behavior?

_____

_____

_____

© 2011 Think Social Publishing, Inc. • www.socialthinking.com

Anger Control Strategies

To control your anger, you have to exercise your BRAIN CONTROL! To do this, you need to choose an ANGER CONTROL strategy. Which one do you think you can use?

1. REALIZE that this is NOT a very big problem, and you could probably just LET IT GO.

2. Work to see it from someone else's point of view so that it's easier to understand what that person is thinking to be able to work together.

3. REMEMBER that being part of a group means you cannot always do it your way or make the decisions you want.

4. Try saying okay to something you don't want to do and then watch how things turn out. Do you get madder or do you calm down?

5. Focus on staying friendly in the group rather than on winning. You "win" if people still want to play with you.

Which strategy did you choose? Did it help you to stay calm?

Did the strategy help you practice brain control?

Why do you think the strategy helped you or didn't help you practice brain control?

If it didn't work, what's another strategy that you could try?

This lesson goes really well with **The Incredible 5-Point Scale** *(Buron and Curtis, 2003).*

Five Points of Showing Anger

1. "OOPS," "DARN IT," "I DON'T LIKE IT."

2. "Grumph," "This makes me so mad!," "I hate doing this," but still with a mostly calm face and voice.

3. STARTING TO YELL, LOUD VOICE, NOT BEING PART OF THE GROUP (getting uncomfortable, others are wondering if they want to be with you).

4. WHINING, STOMPING, REFUSING—frustrating to others!

5. YELLING, RUNNING, SCREAMING, CRYING—Scary!

. . . .

We are all human, and part of being human is making mistakes. Everyone gets angry sometimes. You have control over how you show your anger. We are practicing controlling our anger and showing a 1 or 2 anger level so that other people feel comfortable and want to continue to be around us.

When people have trouble controlling their anger, others tend to remember that. It may then make it harder in the future for a person to feel comfortable being with someone who was not able to control his or her anger.

Helpful Anger and Unhelpful Anger

We may feel mad or angry when something happens to upset us. Not all anger is "bad"; sometimes it helps us focus on what's important to us. However, how we react to our anger can also cause us to "sink or swim." We "sink" if we react in a big way to our anger and are mean to people around us. We "swim" if we feel our anger but stay pretty calm and explain what's upsetting us.

HELPFUL ANGER can:	UNHELPFUL BIG ANGER can:
Make you feel more alert.	Make you focus on being mean to others.
Help you think about what's upsetting you.	Make others not want to help you.
Once you think about what is upsetting, you can better explain it to someone else.	Make you think only about you and not about how others feel.
Help you to focus on what you need to do to calm down your emotions.	Make you feel out of control.
Alert you to threats around you; make you aware if someone is treating you badly.	Make your body really tense.
	Leave a negative impression (create weird or uncomfortable thoughts in others).
Can you think of more?	Can you think of more?

Reacting and Overreacting!

Being with people, even your friends and family, can be annoying at times!

Each of us has our own feelings, our own moods, and our own things we want. When you're young, you're taught that we're all supposed to be FAIR, but at your age you now realize that it's IMPOSSIBLE TO BE FAIR all of the time. Often the person who feels like things are FAIR is the person who is feeling good about the situation!

Working or hanging out as part of a group is important not only for school but also for every part of your life. Figuring out how to be with people without getting SO MAD at them, even when you think things are "not fair," is really important. We all react to people around us because we all have thoughts that lead us to feelings. We react to our feelings about the situation.

Use *feeling words* to describe how you feel and then react to each of the following situations:

1. A person cuts in front of you in line.

2. A person offers you some candy.

3. A teacher does not call on you.

4. Your teacher tells you that you're doing a good job.

5. You get mad at yourself for not knowing something.

6. You get mad because you weren't chosen and you think it's unfair.

7. Your teacher is giving you too much work.

8. Your friends don't seem to be giving you the ball to play.

9. No one seems to be listening to you when you talk.

10. Your teacher gave you and everyone else in the class more homework than YOU wanted.

As you get older, people expect your big emotional reactions to get smaller, even if you still have the same feelings. This means that when someone cuts in line in first grade, you may yell and push them, but by fifth grade you quietly tell the person to go to the back of the line. Whatever grade you are in, you still think it's wrong for someone to cut in line. This may make you feel mad, but you're expected to react in a calmer way as you get older!

Describe what it would look like for you if you OVERREACT. OVERREACTIONS are when people think you're using Big Anger at a time when you should react in a little way even if you have a problem.

_____

_____

Problems are no fun, but we all have to deal with a lot of "NO FUNS" when we're with_____

_____ people.

What strategy do you use to keep yourself from OVERREACTING? You can still feel somewhat sad or mad, but you learn to control the size of your reaction by:

_____

_____

How do you know if it's working? Does it help you to stay calmer if you use a Big Anger reaction or a calm reaction even though you're angry?

_____

_____

If I Am Mad!

It is okay to feel MAD when things happen to us, but it is not okay to make others feel bad if you're mad about something. There are better ways to handle our anger than:

- ## YELLING

- ## HAVING A TANTRUM

- ## HITTING OTHERS

- ## SAYING MEAN OR HURTFUL THINGS TO OTHERS

. . . .

We may have to calm down first to solve the problem. What are some things you can do to calm down when you feel mad so that you can make better choices about how to handle the problem?

1.

2.

3.

4.

Social Thinking® Thinksheets for Tweens and Teens

THINGS That TRIGGER My ANGER

External Triggers	Internal Triggers
Someone makes a face at me.	I tell myself that people will think I'm a coward if I don't fight.
Someone gossips about me.	I tell myself I'm stupid because I failed the last two tests I took.
I fail a test.	I keep thinking about a fight I had with my brother and I get madder and madder.
My teacher keeps me after school.	I tell myself I'm no good at anything.
I get in trouble for something I didn't do.	When I feel sad or frustrated I forget that I can control the way I feel, and I can't stop thinking about it and get really mad.
Can you think of more?	*Can you think of more?*

© 2011 Think Social Publishing, Inc. • www.socialthinking.com

Being Angry Is Okay:
What I Do and Say Is Important EVEN When I'm Angry!

It's okay to feel angry. All people feel angry now and then. As kids get older, they learn safe ways to handle anger. This is very, very, very, very, very important. Handling anger responsibly helps to keep everyone safe.

It's important to *keep thinking about the people in the situation even when I'm angry*. Some people may forget to think about the right thing to do when they're angry. They may make mistakes with their anger. It is a good thing that, as people get older, they learn to make good choices EVEN WHILE THEY ARE ANGRY. As we learn to do this, we demonstrate we're becoming more mature.

Even when kids are very, very, very, very, very angry, they can learn to keep thinking so that they make better choices. Knowing what to think is important.

Here are three things that mature, intelligent young people like me learn to think when they're angry:
1. **I will not be angry for long.** I spend more time feeling okay or good than I do angry. I will feel happy once again.
2. **This problem has a solution.** Talking to others is really the best way to figure out other solutions. When we're angry, our minds are often the most inflexible. Talking to people helps us to think of other ways to handle tough situations.
3. **It's possible to have a bad time during a good day.** Sometimes kids feel angry or sad for a short time but know the good day will return. This is especially true when we make good choices while angry.

When I am angry, I can choose from this list what to say or do:
1. **Take deep breaths or take a break.** Experts on anger say that doing things like taking deep breaths, stretching, or taking a walk increases oxygen to the brain, making it easier to think and make good choices.
2. **Use words to let others know I'm angry.** I may tell others I'm angry by talking or writing things down; I don't have to look angry to feel angry! If I look angry it may make others angry with me!
3. **Keep other people and things safe at all times.** This means keeping my hands, feet, and fingers safely under my control.

Sometimes, kids make serious mistakes with anger. They may decide to kick or hit other people. They may decide to throw things. Sometimes very young children do this. These young children think hitting and kicking lets everyone know how angry they are. When a child gets older and still kicks or hits, people wonder why that child is "acting so young" or "immature." By the time students are in the upper grades of elementary school and middle school, they are expected to make calm, intelligent, safe decisions when they're angry. They are expected to stay in control when in public places. I am learning to do this, too. More and more, I stay calm and keep thinking and working with others when I am angry. This is a very intelligent and mature thing to do!

What helps me calm down?

Emotion Detective

I am working on having more control of my emotions. Knowing what it looks like, feels like, and sounds like when I have different emotions helps me to monitor them. But before I can do this, I am working on being a better Emotion Detective. My job is to observe other people, identify how they are feeling, and, if possible, identify what makes them feel the way they are feeling. I can practice being an Emotion Detective in all kinds of places—at home, at school, and out in the community.

UPSET

Describe one time that I observed another person feeling UPSET:

Guess what made the person feel this way?

What did the person do to show that he or she was feeling UPSET?

Was this a good choice? *(yes/no)* _____

If I were that person, a better choice that the person could have made is:

SAD

One time that I observed another person feeling SAD:

Guess what made the person feel this way?

What did the person do to show that he or she was feeling SAD?

Was this a good choice? *(yes/no)* _____

Is there a better choice that the person could have made?

FRUSTRATED

One time that I observed another person feeling FRUSTRATED:

Guess what made the person feel this way?

What did the person do to show that he or she was feeling FRUSTRATED?

Was this a good choice? *(yes/no)* _____

I think a better choice that the person could have made is:

ANGRY
One time that I observed another person feeling ANGRY:

Guess what made the person feel this way?

What did the person do to show that he or she was feeling ANGRY?

Was this a good choice? *(yes/no)* _____

The better choice I think this person could have made is:

LIVID or Really, Really Upset
One time that I observed another person feeling LIVID:

Guess what made the person feel this way?

What did the person do to show that he or she was feeling LIVID?

Was this a good choice? *(yes/no)* _____

I think a better choice this person could have made is:

When I Am Angry

1. When I catch myself showing my anger in a big way or refusing to work with other people, I am losing control. This means that I am not able to participate with others in a way that is expected. *Give me an example of when this happened:*

2. When this happens, I am now part of a problem. The problem is that I am not able to work in a group or do my work. What is the problem caused by based on the example in the first box?

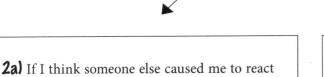

2a) If I think someone else caused me to react in this way, how can I think about it from the other person's point of view? Is there a chance I overreacted and made the problem worse?

2b) If I created the problem because I got mad about something I had to do, what is a strategy I can use to calm down to help the problem get smaller?

3. If you can, use strategies to help yourself calm down and show you're trying to work through the problem. You're now called a problem-solver. Problem-solvers do not make problems go away. Instead, they just help problems to get a bit smaller! *If so, great job!*

Double-Dip Feelings

Feelings can get pretty confusing! You can have two very different feelings at once, which makes them hard to understand. Think of times when you have had both of the feelings described below at the same time!

*Lesson adapted from **Double-Dip Feelings** (Cain and Patterson, 2001).*

HAPPY and **SAD**	
PLAYFUL and **MAD**	
PROUD and **SCARED**	
BRAVE and **AFRAID**	
MEAN and **FRIENDLY**	
EXCITED and **WORRIED**	
HATED and **LOVED**	

And there are plenty more (embarrassed and excited, glad and sorry...). *Can you think of any more?*

Emotional Opposites

Discuss examples of when you experienced feeling two opposite and strong emotions at the same time, or when you observed someone else have this type of reaction to a situation.

. . . .

HAPPY and MAD   **THRILLED and WORRIED**

PROUD and ASHAMED   **HATED and LOVED**

JOYFUL and SAD   **GLAD and SORRY**

BRAVE and AFRAID   **EXCITED and EMBARRASSED**

FRIENDLY and MEAN   **PLEASED and JEALOUS**

Matching Experiences with Facial Expressions to Show Our Emotions

Consider all the things that you have experienced in the past week, month, or year, and make a note to match an experience with an emotion.

Feeling fine:	Feeling good:	Feeling bummed:	Feeling relief:
Feeling frustrated:	Looking forward to something happening:	Feeling embarrassed:	Feeling nervous about something people expect you to do well:
Feeling overwhelmed:	Feeling proud:	Feeling someone was rude to you:	Feeling obnoxious or goofy:
Feeling angry:	Feeling excited:	Feeling that someone was unfair to you:	Feeling weary or tired:

When we have feelings, we may actually show how we feel through our facial expressions while we explain a situation to someone. *For example*, if we tell someone we did really poorly on a test and look sad at the same time, the person will understand we felt sad about doing poorly on a test.

Now that you have isolated experiences to go with each emotion, talk about each experience and match your facial expression to help people understand how you felt in each situation. *Creative tip:* It's fun to make a videotape of yourself and others trying to show how you and they would express two emotions at once!

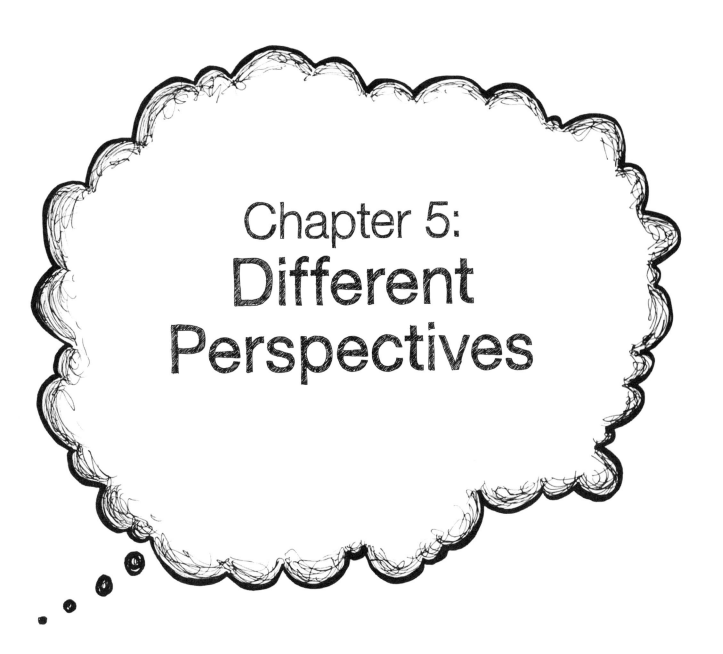

Chapter 5:
Different Perspectives

The lessons in this section that relate to making impressions were inspired from lessons in *Social Skill Strategies: A Social-Emotional Curriculum for Adolescents, Book A,* pages 116-121 (Gajewski, N., Hirn, P., and Mayo, P., 1998). This book is an excellent resource for many lessons.

THINKING and SAYING Are TWO DIFFERENT THINGS!

THINKING ABOUT HOW OTHER PEOPLE THINK...

1. I consider my thoughts.

2. I consider how they'll make my listener feel.

3. I revise my words that represent my thoughts based on how I want the other person to respond to me!

The words I say send a message to the listener:

If I want to make the person feel good, I choose words that do that. I can also choose words that can hurt someone, if I want to do that. The problem comes when I say words that are unexpected or hurt someone when I don't mean to do that.

Brain Filters

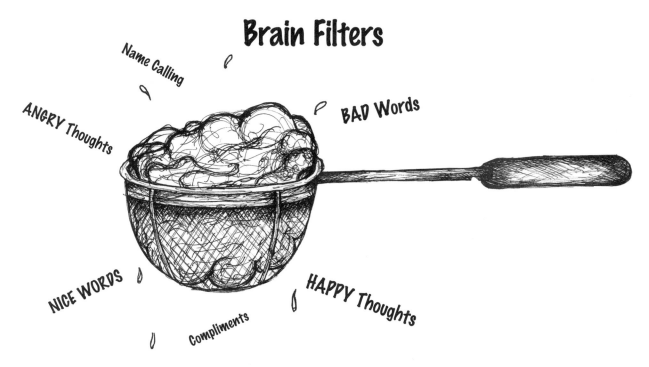

Brain filters help us to filter our thoughts so that when we use our words to speak our thoughts, they don't hurt other people's feelings or offend them. Sometimes you use your brain filter and you don't even realize it! Sometimes you don't use your brain filter and this can get you in trouble with other people!

Saying things to people that upset or offend them can cause problems for you. Why? What do you think some of those problems could be?

Can you think of a time when you really need to use your brain filter?

Can you think of a time when you forgot to use your brain filter? What happened?

What do you imagine your brain filter looks like? *Draw a picture.*

Let's Practice Using Our Brain Filter!

In the following situations, people forgot to use their brain filters. *Try to locate when this happened in each situation.*

Scenario 1: Nick and **Matt** are friends and are playing video games after school.

Nick: "Wow, you almost got the highest score on Halo 2. How did you do that?"

Matt: "Yeah, my brother taught me how to cheat the computer!"

Nick: "Do you think your brother could teach me?"

Matt: "No—I don't think he has the time. Besides you're not really good at video games, so my brother wouldn't want to teach you."

Scenario 2: Jesse, Alex, and **Mark** are sitting together during lunch in the school cafeteria.

Jesse: "Hey Alex, do you want to come over this weekend and play football?"

Alex: "Sure I'd love to come!"

Mark: "That sounds like fun. I'll be there too!"

Jesse: "Uhhh–Mark, I thought you didn't like football."

Mark: "No, I do. It's just that I'm still learning how to play."

Alex: "Hey look, I just don't think you're good enough to play with us."

Mark: "Oh—okay, I guess I could do homework instead this weekend."

Jesse: "That's a good idea—we do have a lot of math homework."

Scenario 3: You're sitting in class during a really boring history lesson.

Teacher: "Let me continue for another 20 minutes with this lesson and then the whole class can take a break."

You: *(mumbled under your breath)* "If this teacher keeps talking, I'll be so bored I'll fall asleep."

Teacher: *(to you)* "Excuse me, did you have something to add to the discussion today?"

You: "Uh–no, I just said that I thought the discussion was interesting."

Teacher: "Oh great, then you can lead the discussion for the next 20 minutes of class!"

Now let's role play the situations. Using your *brain filter*, change the words used so that no one was offended, and then describe how that changes the size of or eliminates the problem.

Turning On Your Brain Filter

One important thing to practice is keeping our brain filter turned on—thinking about how what we say will make another person feel before we say it. We have to think about whether it will make another person have a good thought or a weird or uncomfortable thought.

If it will make another person have a weird thought, we can either change what we were going to say or how we were going to say it. It's best to keep hurtful or negative words in your head so that people keep having good thoughts about you!

Keeping your brain filter turned on is hard work and takes practice.

When is one time that you used your brain filter today?

_____

Did you keep the thought in your head or change what you were going to say or how you were going to say it?

_____

How did this make the other person feel?

_____

When is one time that you forgot to keep your brain filter turned on?

_____

Should you have changed what you said or how you said it? Or should you have kept the thought in your head?

_____

How did this make the other person feel?

_____

What can you do in the future to help you remember to keep your brain filter turned on?

_____

People Are Always Thinking About Us, and We Are Always Thinking About Them

People are expected to notice each other and even think about each other when they're together in the same area. You don't have to be talking, hanging out, or playing with people for them to have a thought about you and for you to have a thought about them.

We have thoughts about what people look like, how they're behaving, and what they're doing. We also have thoughts about what they may be saying to someone (even if they're not talking with us).

. . . .

Consider how your own brain does this!

Think of some times in school when you heard some other kids talking and you thought about what they were saying to each other.

Think of a time when you didn't like what a kid said.

Think of a time when you thought a kid was cool because of what you heard her say or what you watched her do.

. . . .

Everyone has thoughts about other people, all the time. If someone is quiet, that doesn't mean people won't have any thoughts about the quiet person. They still notice the person is there and may even think that he doesn't seem to like to talk to people.

Because you notice that you think about people around you, it makes sense that they think about you as well. These are not great big, huge thoughts. It's just that we all notice each other. When people do what's expected, people barely notice them at all. When kids do what is "unexpected," they tend to get a lot more attention, whether they want it or not!

How We Think About EACH OTHER!

At school we're around people all the time. Why is it so important at school to be aware of the thoughts we all have about each other? How do you think being aware that we all think about each other helps most students to control the way they act in front of other kids, even when sitting in class?

Read the following situations. Think about the impressions being made in the scenarios and how these change the way kids think about and then treat each other.

Role play some of these situations and then discuss how the people are thinking about each other. Can you think of ways in which one of the students in each scenario can change his or her behavior to blend in better with the other kids?

Situation: During lunchtime, Johnny is talking to Tommy and uses all kinds of scientific, intellectual words in the conversation. What impression do you think he's making on Tommy? Why?

_____

Situation: Sam doesn't like the game that the boys have to play in PE. So he decides to fold his arms, walk along the inside of the field, and daydream about what he'll talk about with his Dungeon and Dragons friends at lunch. What impression do you think he is making on the kids in his PE class?

_____

_____

What should he try to do instead to keep others thinking good thoughts about him?

_____

_____

Situation: Jasmine decides to interrupt a conversation that's already going on, by charging into the group and repeating, "Lunchtime, lunchtime, I am so hungry!" What impression is she making on the kids in the group?

_____

_____

Who else might be having "weird" thoughts about her?

_____

People are always thinking about us! You don't even have to say anything with your words and they probably still "think about you."

This is about IMPRESSIONS. People think about you, and you think about others based on:

- ***What we say***

- ***What we do***

- ***How we look***

Think about the messages you send (IMPRESSIONS) to others and what you do to send those messages.

Some people who have thoughts about you:	What do they think about you?	Why do they think this?
Teacher		
Therapist		
Brother		
Sister		
Grandmother		
Dog		
Other students in your classroom		

Rating Your Own Impression

Below are some things to watch out for when you're around others. This should help you figure out what impression you make on others.

Rate yourself on how you did with your ability to make a good impression on others. (Use two situations, such as coming into the classroom and working as part of a class.)

Rate yourself on the items below.	*Great, I did this well.* (10 points)		*Average, I was okay sometimes.* (5 points)		*Oops, I didn't do this well.* (-5 points)	
	#1	#2	#1	#2	#1	#2
Showed an interested, calm body posture, sat upright						
Looked at the group members						
Kept comments related to what others are doing or thinking about						
Stayed out of people's personal space						
Used an inside voice						
Used a friendly tone when talking with others						
Facial expressions sent good messages—having a good time, friendly, interested, excited if winning a game						
Comments were respectful toward others (friendly, related to topic)						
Subtotal						
Overall impression I made on the others:					**Total score:**	

© 2011 Think Social Publishing, Inc. • www.socialthinking.com

Anxiety, Social Thoughts, and What You Can Do to Help Yourself Be Included

We all have thoughts about each other. This, in part, helps us to stay safe by recognizing what people are doing when they are around us and how they may be feeling. If we see someone who may try to hurt us or someone who is in a very bad mood, we try and get away from them!

Social observation

From a social participation perspective, we notice how others behave around us. We observe what people are doing and we may change how we are behaving based on what we see others thinking about and/or how they are feeling. Think about students in your class. How many can you think of who:

- Talk too much? *List the number_____*
- Barely talk at all? *List the number_____*
- Look like they are trying to show off around other students? *List the number_____*
- Are really smart? *List the number _____*
- Look like they have difficulty learning? *List the number _____*
- Forget to turn in their homework? *List the number_____*
- Appear to be a student the teacher really likes? *List the number _____*

If you cannot answer the above questions, begin to observe the students around you more closely and then try answering the questions again. All of us should be able to notice at least one student in each of the above categories.

Thoughts come in different sizes

Because the mind was designed to notice other people and what they are doing around us, it makes sense that all people have thoughts about each other! However, sometimes we wish people were not thinking about us.

Small thoughts/feelings

For sure, it would feel more relaxing to be able to be around others and not have to think about what they are thinking about us. But, this is just a wish and not reality. This means it is important to realize that most of the time we are around people, we have very small thoughts about each other. In fact, we barely notice people if they are doing behaviors that are expected across different situations. When we barely notice others, we describe this by saying we are having very small thoughts about these people.

Medium size thoughts/feelings

However, sometimes we do notice what people are doing around us. When people's behavior attracts our attention, it is often because they are doing something that is unusual for the situation. They can do something that is really good or they can do something that people think of as unexpected in a negative way for the situation. When this happens, we more actively notice these people, and this means we are having medium size thoughts and emotions about them.

Large thoughts/feelings

When people around us do something that is very unexpected, it tends to make us have strong uncomfortable thoughts and likely strong negative emotions about that person in that situation. We can describe this as having a very large thought and emotion about another person.

Social anxiety and our thoughts

People who develop strong social anxiety tend to wish people did not think about them at all! Often they become frustrated that people are thinking about them, as they feel this adds to their social anxiety.

Tips on keeping others' thoughts small about you, even when you are anxious

When you, as a person with social anxiety, wish people did not have thoughts about you, learn about and try to behave in a manner that is expected for the situation. This may help prevent you from feeling so frustrated and anxious as you learn that people do not notice you in a large thought way.

Exploring when social anxiety leads others to have larger thoughts about you

There may be times when your social anxiety makes you feel that you should try to avoid participating in the same way as your peers in a situation. You may refuse to talk or look at others or you may move your body away from others to try to stay out of a group you want to avoid. Your feelings may then lead to more anxiety. When this happens, others may start to notice that you are not doing what is expected so they may start to have medium size thoughts about your behavior!

What is a socially anxious person to do?

Socially anxious people usually have strong self-awareness that they are being perceived by others, but they don't know how to put those thoughts into a system that works to help them stay calm in the presence of others. Instead, they tend to worry more than they would like about how people are thinking about them. By accident, this makes them spend more time observing how anxious they feel rather than observing how others are relating around them and how they could possibly join in.

People with social anxiety want to be included; their brains just don't make this as easy for them! Instead their brains keep them from easily and realistically observing what others are doing and thinking with each other to interact, and their brains also make them unrealistically think that people are thinking about them in a negative way! When the socially anxious person gets stuck thinking too much about people's negative thoughts, it tends to make them more anxious!

If you are socially anxious, you can work at helping yourself fit in by trying to shift your observations away from your own negative worries about how people are thinking about you and to instead focus more on what others are doing and what you would like to do with them. Start to observe how they are hanging out and also how they contribute to what others are doing or saying.

To help yourself increase your focus on what others are doing and how you can help yourself to join them and to focus less on observing your own anxiety, begin by taking some deep breaths to help yourself calm down and refocus your observation. Then, shift your focus from yourself to others. You don't have to actually interact with anyone else at this point, but it will help you to learn to watch what others are realistically doing and how they talk to each other. This will help you think about ways in which you too can eventually feel comfortable participating in this way! You can help yourself to make the more positive social impressions you want to make!

The Art of Eating with Others

We make impressions when we're with others by:

- *How we look*

- *What we say*

- *What we do*

One time we make impressions is when we eat in the company of others. There are a lot of unwritten rules about how to eat in front of others. Can you think of three?

1.

2.

3.

Talking and eating takes a lot more work than just eating or just talking. Here are some things to think about:

- Pacing
- Amount of the portion that you serve yourself
- Cleanliness as you eat *(keeping your face and hands clean)*
- What you do when the food is running out and you want more
- Paying attention to the topic when you're with others
- Paying attention to others with your eyes
- Making comments to others between swallows
- Asking questions to others between swallows

When you're with someone else while you eat, what are some things you can think about?

What are some of your own eating behaviors you can monitor to try and make a better impression?

What's COOL at School

We make impressions by how we look. Even when we don't say a word, people form thoughts about us based on:

What we wear: Do your clothes look like they should be worn together? Are your clothes too short? Too tight? Do you match the situation? Casual (school, the beach)? Nice Casual (a school event or a family party)? Formal (special occasion, such as a formal wedding or a fancy restaurant)?

What we are NOT wearing: Do you look like the rest of the group? At school, it is usually a problem if you don't wear shoes or, if you are a boy, you don't wear a shirt or, if you are a girl, you expose too much of your torso or legs etc. People have thoughts about that, and you might get called to the office.

Hygiene: Do you have body odor or do your clothes smell? Does your hair look clean and pretty neat? Have you been brushing your teeth?

What do you see kids wearing that make a good or cool impression?

1.

2.

3.

4.

If you wear a uniform for school, can you still make a good or not-so-good impression? How?

_____

How do you make an impression by NOT WEARING something? Do you look like the rest of the group?

_____

Tell about a time when you made a good impression by how you looked:

_____

Tell about a time when you made a not-so-good impression by how you looked or for not being clean, etc.:

_____

IMPRESSIONS–Think About It at Home Before You Go to School!

This week, you can use this chart to keep track of the impressions you made by *How You Looked*. Every day, keep track of your clothing and hygiene and figure out what type of impression this will make on others. *Your parent can add notes too.*

Also, you're in charge of spying on others at school to observe what impressions they might be making on others at school, including you.

	Monday	Tuesday	Wednesday	Thursday	Friday	What Impression Are You Making on Others?
What are you wearing?						*For Mom or Dad:*
Do the colors go together?						*For Mom or Dad:*
Do your clothes look neat?						*For Mom or Dad:*
Did you brush your hair before school?						*For Mom or Dad:*
Did you brush your teeth?						*For Mom or Dad:*
Did you use deodorant?						*For Mom or Dad:*

Social Thinking® *Thinksheets for Tweens and Teens*

Who at school made a good impression on you by how they looked?

_____

_____

_____

Why did you have this thought?

_____

_____

_____

Who at school made a not-so-good impression on you by how they looked?

_____

_____

_____

Why did you have this thought?

_____

_____

_____

Know the Boundaries of Other People's Minds!

What are boundaries?

1. They mark the territory we shouldn't cross.

2. They're invisible.

3. We can cross people's physical and mental boundaries.

   - **Physical boundaries** have to do with where we put our bodies.
   - **Mental boundaries** have to do with what we're thinking about and what we let people know.

4. If you cross a boundary, people may feel uncomfortable and have a strange thought about you.

. . . .

There are topics that you can talk about and topics that you should not talk about...only because they make other people uncomfortable. Some of the boundaries might have to do with:

- Weight/physical appearance
- Grades (especially if you get good ones)
- Religion
- Politics
- Clothing choice
- School choice
- Hobbies choice
- Pointing out someone's disability

What else can you think of?

These boundaries mean "tread carefully"...they don't mean don't talk about the topic at all. It just means to realize that you need to proceed cautiously and use lots of "thinking with your eyes" to make sure you're not making the other person uncomfortable.

To SPEAK or NOT to SPEAK — That Is the Question

When you talk with others, you need to think about your words and the message your body is sending so that the person can keep feeling good about you and have good thoughts about you. The trick is to really think about the words you're about to say and ask yourself if these words would be hurtful to or insult the other person. IF SO, YOU WANT TO KEEP THOSE WORDS IN YOUR MIND AND NOT SAY THEM.

. . . .

TO SPEAK or NOT TO SPEAK FORMULA:

IF THE WORDS WILL BE HURTFUL OR INSULTING = KEEP THEM IN YOUR MIND

. . . .

Let's practice thinking about the words and the body language the following messages will send:

1. Johnny told Matthew, "I like working on projects with Teresa more than with you." What would Matthew think? So…

    TO SPEAK OR NOT TO SPEAK?

2. Nick told Sam, using a FRUSTRATED TONE, "I don't like sitting next to you because you talk too much." What would Sam think? So…

    TO SPEAK OR NOT TO SPEAK?

3. Jane said to Ryan, "I think your hair looked better the other way. Now you look goofy." What might Ryan think? So…

    TO SPEAK OR NOT TO SPEAK?

Sometimes we may really want to tell someone something—maybe because we think it would be helpful. If that happens, what do we do? Let's try to rephrase the statements so that they don't insult the other person or hurt anyone's feelings.

1. Johnny told Matthew, _____

_____

2. Nick told Sam, using a _____ tone, _____

_____

3. Jane said to Ryan, _____

_____

Being Sensitive to World Cultures and Religions

Gestures considered friendly in one land might be offensive in another. For example, in Australia, an enthusiastic thumbs-up sign does not mean someone is having a good thought about something. It actually means someone is mad at you! It's wise to learn a little about other countries before you visit them or when you're making friends or hanging out with people from other cultures so you don't end up in trouble when you think you're giving someone a compliment.

Awareness of different religions is also important. Everyone has their own personal spiritual beliefs that may differ from your own. Be aware of these differences and remain respectful! To show respect, this means you would not say any comments about a religion or a God unless you're sure that the other person shares your religious belief. For this reason, people mostly talk about religion at home or in a place where they come together to practice their religion.

Here are some *examples* of ways that rituals, greetings, and friendship vary from country to country:

- Many Latinos, Asians, and people in Middle Eastern and Mediterranean countries consider same-sex hand-holding or arm-linking a sign of friendship. They would be amazed to learn that these gestures may be interpreted in America as signs of homosexuality.

- Japanese people bow as a form of greeting. They disapprove of public displays of affection (touching each other), even between husbands and wives.

- People in Sri Lanka, India, Bangladesh, and Thailand greet each other by placing their hands in a prayer-like position in front of their chins and nodding their heads.

- Most people in France, Italy, Spain, and other Mediterranean countries kiss each other on both cheeks in greeting.

- Because many Asians believe that a person's soul resides in the head, the American custom of patting a child's head is seen as threatening.

- Americans are taught to look each other in the eye when speaking. Children who are raised in an Asian culture may have been taught that it's respectful to avoid eye contact. In culturally diverse schools in the United States, teachers may misinterpret a student's avoidance of eye contact as a mark of disrespect, when in fact it may be the opposite. In some urban schools, direct eye contact between teenagers may be a sign someone is giving you a challenge, which may lead to a fight.

- While the term "Jesus Christ" is used by some people as slang to indicate frustration, this can be insulting to a Christian person who may believe a holy name is being used inappropriately.

When we're careful about what we say or do by thinking about another person's culture or religion, this is called *"being sensitive."*

When we feel bad because someone is "insensitive" to our differing points of view or experiences, this is called *"being offended."*

What are some cultural and religious rules you have noticed in your community?

Have you been offended by someone being insensitive to your culture or religion?

How do you monitor your own behavior to make sure you're sensitive to others' differences, which helps you to avoid being offensive?

Joking About Others' Religion and/or Culture: The Hidden Rules

. . . .

You probably hear your peers from the same culture, ethnic group, or religion make fun of themselves or use negative words to talk about their own culture or religion.

There is a hidden rule for peers that share the same culture, ethnic group, and/or religion: They can make fun of their cultures, ethnicities, or religions when they're together.

This means, for example, you may hear Christians making fun of Christians, Jews making fun of Jews, African Americans making fun of African Americans, or Whites making fun of Whites.

However, if you're hanging out with a group, but you do not actually belong to the culture or religion they're making fun of, you are NOT allowed to make fun of it yourself!

Just because you hear people who are a part of that group using this form of humor does NOT mean you can use the same jokes or name-calling. You should not do this unless you're part of the same culture or religion that is being made fun of!

And even if you are part of that culture or religion, you cannot tease endlessly. An invisible line exists with which things said are funny once but when repeated more often, seem no longer funny and can even be interpreted as insulting.

So the *real rule* is, if you question whether you should say something, or you wonder if you have joked about it too much, keep yourself from saying it at all.

What It Means to Be Respectful

Being respectful of others is part of what it takes to work as part of a group, whether it's a big or a small group. While it's easy to say the word "respect," it's harder to understand what it means.

"Respect" or "being respectful" is a concept. Concepts are words that don't mean just one thing—instead they describe many things that are supposed to happen at once.

Here are some of the many things that are supposed to happen at once to "be respectful" to your classmates, your teacher, your parent, etc.

- Act politely. This means you behave in a way that shows you're thinking about the people around you. For example, you may allow someone to go in front of you, or say "hi," or smile when you're thinking about or acknowledging someone.
- Look interested when someone is talking.
- Speak using a tone of voice that sounds friendly.
- Refrain from using your words or actions to make someone feel bad by implying that you're smarter than him or her.
- Offer help to someone who you see may need it and accept help from someone when she notices that you may be having difficulty accomplishing something.
- Notice how people feel. If they're sad or frustrated, adjust your own behavior to help them feel better or to calm down (this is also called "being compassionate").
- If someone states an idea or opinion with which you disagree, hold your thoughts in your head until you're sure it's the right time and the right place to share your thoughts.

When someone is not being respectful in a group, the group is no longer working together well. It frustrates other group members when someone doesn't let the group work together as a group. This "disrespectful behavior" is seen as causing frustration to members of the group. This is why they may ask the person who is perceived as "being disrespectful" to leave the group. By having the person leave, the group gets to work better together, and it also helps people to feel calmer emotions.

To summarize:
Being respectful is not one thing! This term represents many behaviors that happen simultaneously. Sometimes it's hard to do all these things right all the time. This is why we have special times to practice how to work as parts of groups. You have probably heard it said before, but we'll say it once more:

TO GET RESPECT, YOU HAVE TO GIVE RESPECT.

Because we all want to be treated with respect, we all have to practice giving it! And this does take practice.

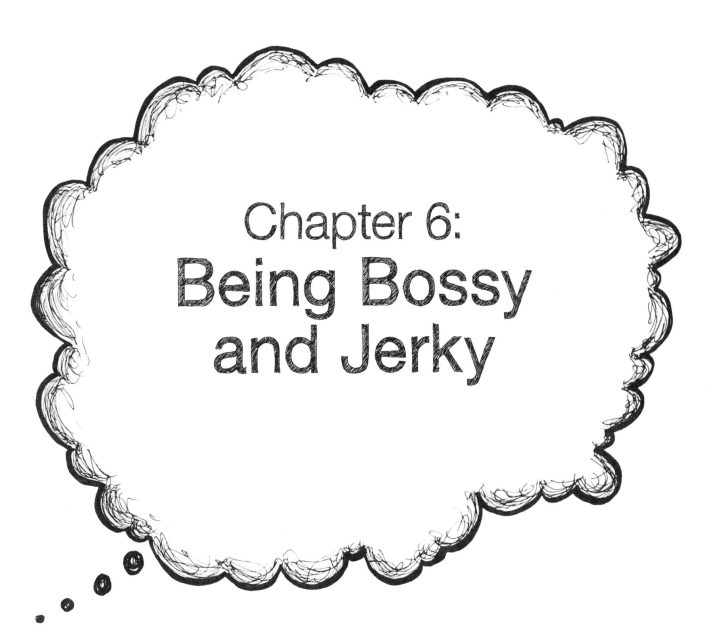

Don't Wake Up Your Inner Jerk!

Each of us likes to be thought of in good ways by others. We like people to think we're nice, smart, and other good things like that.

However, every one of us also has a hidden jerk lurking inside. When our jerk wakes up, he makes us do things that make others feel bad or at least uncomfortable when we're around. Or someone else's jerk makes that person do or say things that make us feel bad. When a person makes another person feel bad, that person's inner jerk is often awakened as well.

When you wake up the hidden jerk in the other person, it's called "feeding the jerk jerk food." Once that person's inner jerk is awake, it often makes the person do or say things that make you feel bad as well. Your two jerks then continue to behave in jerky ways towards each other. This is called "being stuck in the Kingdom of Jerkdom together"!

When we're with others, our job is to try and control our inner hidden lurking jerk so we don't wake up the jerk in others. Getting stuck in the Kingdom of Jerkdom is no fun for anyone!

Because it took both of you to get stuck in the Kingdom, it will take both of you to leave the Kingdom together.

You can help find the exit door to the Kingdom of Jerkdom by putting a stop to your own jerk's behavior. Don't do or say anything that will continue to keep the other person's jerk awake. As you calm down your own jerk, you get to walk closer to the exit door. It helps the other person keep his or her own jerk calm as well. Once both jerks are calm, you get to leave the Kingdom of Jerkdom and return to the place where you find being with others helps to keep you calm and focused. Don't wake up your inner jerk!

Every one of us can cause a problem for someone else. While most of us like to be thought of in a good way most of the time, we all can be difficult to live and work with some of the time.

If WE DO and SAY THINGS that make SOMEONE ELSE UPSET or at least A LITTLE BIT UNCOMFORTABLE, we have AWOKEN the INNER JERK that LURKS WITHIN ALL OF US!

JERKS: Them, Us, and the Kingdom of Jerkdom!

Here is some honest talk about who jerks are and how we may become one ourselves!

Kids are often difficult in middle school and high school. In middle school, kids seem to be the MOST difficult. Each one of us can be a difficult person in the eyes of others.

What makes people difficult? *Here are some ideas:*

- **Being mean:**
  People get our attention by saying or doing things to us that are upsetting.
- **Ignoring us:**
  People ignore us when they pay attention to others. People dismiss what we say and act like we don't exist.
- **Making us feel stupid:**
  People make comments about what we say that make us feel like they think we're stupid.
- **Acting sneaky:**
  People act really nice to others or around teachers and then do things we perceive of as mean only when others aren't looking.
- **Lying:**
  Jerks lie. They try and make people think things that aren't true to make us look bad or at least to make themselves look better.
- **What else?**

The reality is that none of us are "saints" and each of us has been a difficult person to someone else, whether it's our friend, acquaintance, someone we don't know, our sibling, and others in our families.

Here are some things we need to do to handle the difficult person or difficult moment in our life:

1. **Deal with anxiety:**

   a. All of us wear anxiety some part of each day, if not all day, like a sweater.

   b. We need to be able to appreciate that all people feel some level of social anxiety. Work on strategies with your teacher, counselor, or parent to help you accept that you can become anxious without letting it stop you from thinking clearly about how to react and respond to others in a way that keeps people feeling pretty good about you.

   c. We're still in control even when we're anxious. Being a little bit anxious is something that most of us get used to. Even though we're "wearing it," we don't let it take us over.

2. **Realize the person who you are talking to, the one who is treating you like a jerk,** has his own jerk coming awake inside of him. He may even have started all this by having fed you jerk food! Perhaps the person is just having a jerky moment himself or he may be a real jerk. Think of ways to combat the jerk inside your own head when you have to talk to this person:

a. Talk to yourself silently inside your head, and tell yourself the person is a jerk and the best way to deal with a jerk is not to feed him jerk food. Basically, don't respond to what's being said. You're using your Inner Coach when you can coach yourself to avoid feeding the person jerk food.

b. Jerks thrive off jerk food. *Examples* of jerk food include:

   i. Telling the jerk that he's wrong, you're not a jerk. Any attempt to try to convince the jerk that you're not a jerk feeds jerk food to the jerk!

   ii. Accusing the jerk of lying. We know jerks lie—that's part of what makes them jerks. Don't try and convince a jerk that you know she's lying; it's very hard to prove that someone is lying. Just KNOW that she's lying and realize this person is not your friend. Use your Inner Coach and avoid talking to her any further.

   iii. Correcting the jerk and telling him that he doesn't know what he's talking about.

   iv. Deciding that because she's treating you badly, you'll do the same back to her (for example, if she swears at you, you swear back; if she pushes you, you push back).

   v. Getting really upset and showing big emotions. Unfortunately, this feeds the jerk a huge amount of jerk food.
   - The rule in middle school is that we all feel strong emotions but you don't show your strong emotions! If you're upset, still try and act calm and then go find an adult to talk to. You're expected to talk to adults about things that upset you at school.
   - If you have a group of friends who also think this other person is a jerk, you can also talk to them about it, but try to keep your body and face calm. Just use angry words to tell your friends what a jerk the jerk is! Most adults won't advise you to do this, but this is what kids in middle school do a lot with each other; they complain with their friends about other people who aren't in their circle of friends.

   vi. Going to an adult in the presence of the jerk and telling on the jerk. You should go to the adult but not in the presence of the jerk.
   - The rule is you tell an adult in a place away from other students. You explain not only what you think the person did wrong but also how you feel about it. However, in middle school, you're not supposed to cry about it (most of the time). If you do cry, it should not last long (1–2 minutes).

3. **Finally, realize that being a jerk can be contagious.** A real jerk starts to make you act like a jerk right back.

   a. AVOID this trap. The ability to avoid it is called "taking the high road"; it's also called "maturity."

   b. Tell yourself that you know he's a jerk and you can step away. Move your chair, ask to leave the room—just don't feed the jerk jerk food!

If you do get trapped feeding jerk food to the jerk, you probably have become a jerk yourself, and you're both stuck in the Kingdom of Jerkdom together!

Could I Be a Bully?

We like to think that people are either good or bad, that they are either bullies or they are not, but this is not really the truth.

Sometimes people who bully others are people that others think are really nice, sweet, and cooperative. It's not uncommon that someone who bullies another kid on campus may be a teacher's favorite student. It is also very possible that a person who bullies may be a good student or even someone that was a good friend to you at a different time.

Bullies are people who make other people feel bad for no clear reason. They try and hurt someone's feelings or hurt them physically. They may laugh or react to the pain they caused the other person by seeming to enjoy how bad they made that person feel. They're more likely to act like this when they can bully another person while their "friends" observe. This is called "showing off to others."

Bullies are complicated because they're not always bad people, but they're doing bad things in that moment.

Why do bullies bully in that moment? It may be because they want to act tough or get attention. They also may be jealous or may feel bad about themselves, so they want to make others feel bad too. There are many different reasons why people bully, but no reason makes it okay! It's never okay to try and make another person feel bad to make the bully feel more powerful. No one benefits from that kind of made-up power. Bullies often don't realize that the people who see them bully may be laughing on the outside…but on the inside they often have thoughts that the bully is really a jerk!

One thing we all have in common is that we HATE being bullied!!

The really tricky thing about all of this is that some students who have been bullied are also bullies to others. It's possible that even you can be a bully at times! It's not uncommon for us to bully a sister or brother or even a pet.

Being bullied does not give you or any of us permission to bully! To move away from letting the bully in us come out, we have to think about how the other person thinks and feels…and then think about ourselves. Would we want anyone to treat us this way?

Social Thinking requires us to imagine how we make others feel and then choose to monitor our own behaviors in a way so that people feel okay being around us. By continuing to work on this, we work on our own bully prevention, keeping ourselves from being perceived as a bully by others.

For more information on this topic, please see Allen Beane's book, **A Bully Free Classroom**.

Targets Come in Different Sizes!

When people treat you badly, it may mean you're doing something to annoy them. However, people can be mistreated for doing absolutely nothing to deserve it.

Here are some descriptions of people who have not made others feel bad but still are treated badly.

Small Target

By being human we all wear some size target on us for bullies or jerks to zoom in on. Sometimes we're just in the wrong place at the wrong time and a group of bullies makes fun of us just for walking by them. We did nothing to attract their attention and deserve their mean actions.

We will call this a "small size target." If you wear a small target and someone bullies you, he or she should be seriously punished. This is NOT okay!!

Medium Target

A medium target is created when a person does something that others perceive as annoying, making people feel a little uncomfortable when they're around that person. Usually people are medium size targets when they do things that are unexpected in specific situations. Some examples include: a student constantly raises her hand in class and gets annoyed when she is not called on to give the answer. The other students perceive this student thinks she is smarter than everyone else, and this makes everyone else uncomfortable. Another example of a medium size target is a person who turns people in during lunchtime for not following all the campus rules; kids hate it when a peer tells on them to adults for something that was not considered a big deal.

People who wear medium targets on themselves cannot simply blame others for mistreating them; they have to learn that they are doing some behaviors that others find very annoying. People may interpret that the person wearing the medium size target was trying to show people he or she was better than them.

This means that teachers and parents need to discourage people from treating anyone badly and teach them ways in which they can behave that keep those around them feeling comfortable and calm. This means that all the kids who were stuck treating each other in a less than satisfactory way need to work on improving their behavior, including the kid who wears the medium size target!

Large Size Target

You wear a large size target if people perceive you as acting directly mean to others. You in effect, bully them or are feeding them so much jerk food they feel they have to get back at you. An example of wearing a large size target would be if you told someone that they are stupid, ugly, dumb, etc. or, if you hurt someone or yelled at him, etc. Those who wear large size targets are engaging in behaviors that WILL result in people being mean to them. Even if the person who wears the large size target feels he is mistreated because he notices people being mean to him, teachers and parents need to try and help this student to realize that his behavior was a trigger for being treated so poorly!

Students have a social memory for how people made them feel. If Joe wears the large size target and Joe told Mary on Monday that she was stupid and he could not believe how dumb her answers were in class, it's very unlikely Mary will forget this. She may not do anything mean to Joe for many days…then on Friday a whole group of kids, which includes Mary, is now mean to Joe. Joe may say he is "being bullied," but in fact Joe is being treated poorly now because Mary remembered and she told all her friends. Now they have ganged up on Joe! Was Mary right to do this? NO! Was Joe right to be so mean to Mary? No.

So what are the adults to do? They need to hold everyone accountable! Everyone gets in trouble for this. Joe is not innocent but neither are Mary and her friends.

Getting along with people at school means using your thought filter to keep people from feeling you're mean to them. Once people think you're acting mean, they'll return the meanness!

Do You Wear a Medium or LARGE Size Target?

Sometimes we might do things with our bodies or our words that draw attention to us and make us a target for teasing or someone who kids don't want to hang around. We have to remember that people are always thinking about us based on what we do with our bodies or what we say with our words. Let's list some **unexpected behaviors** we have seen others do at school—or that *you* have done at school—that could make someone a target.

What silly or rude things could be done with our BODIES to make us a target at school?

Why don't we want to be a target at school?

_____

_____

How will you feel about yourself if you're not a target?

_____

_____

What will others think about you if you remember to do EXPECTED THINGS when you're with them?

_____

_____

You MIGHT be a Medium or Large Size Target for Teasing, Bullying, or Gossip if you:

- Blurt out information
- Raise your hand all the time (*teacher's pet*)
- Interrupt
- Get too close to other people
- Yell out your answers or responses
- Correct others
- Bully the teacher

- Use too much or inappropriate sarcasm
- Take revenge on others
- Sing or whistle at inappropriate times
- Talk to yourself
- Do odd things with your body
- Finish other people's sentences
- Use a rude tone of voice

How to Stick Up for Yourself with Your Words

1. **To avoid problems:** Tell others what you want–don't grab, don't yell, just tell them!

2. **If there is a problem:**

   USE: *"Tell 'em how you feel"* and *"Tell 'em what you want."*

   STATEMENTS:

   a. I feel angry when you hit me because it hurts. I want you to stop hitting me.

   b. I feel angry when you tease me. It hurts my feelings! I want you to stop teasing me.

3. **"Leave me alone!" "Stop doing that!"**

Tip #1: **Tell people what you want and need** before there is a problem, during a problem, and after a problem!

Tip #2: **Use a medium tone of voice**—not too LOUD and not too soft. Make sure you sound neutral, not MAD or HAPPY.

Tip #3: **Make suggestions,** not demands or threats.

WHAT NOT TO DO:

1. **Don't yell and argue or use an angry tone of voice.**

2. **Don't make demands or threats.**

Bodies Colliding: Bumps or Bullies?

THIS INVOLVES USING OUR FLEXIBLE BRAIN!

It also involves thinking with our eyes to figure out people's plans!

People's bodies move. Sometimes they move into other bodies even when they don't mean or plan to touch the other person. People bump into or push other people *by accident* because their body or clothing or sports equipment or book got in the way of another, or maybe they just weren't looking. If someone bumps into you, that does not automatically mean that the person is being mean. It may mean that the person wasn't aware of how close his body was to yours at the time of the accident. It could also mean you were not paying close attention to the other person. When people touch us or bump into us by accident (not on purpose), we call this *ACCIDENTAL BUMPS OR PUSHES*.

Some people like to touch other people as a way of showing that they like another person as a friend. You will even see football players do this when they pat someone on the shoulder or bottom—it's a way to let them know that they did a good job or a way to show that they understand that the person made a mistake. When people plan to touch the other person to communicate that they're being friendly or understand that the other person made a mistake, they expect that the other person understands that they mean the touch or bump as a good thing. These brief touches or bumps should be interpreted as being friendly.

Sometimes people use their bodies in unfriendly ways on purpose. Often, this is when a person has an *unfriendly face* and *goes out of his or her way to touch you in a way that was intended to cause you harm.* A person who does this to you or others may be mad at you in response to something that you did, but this person can also do this to you when you don't even really know this person or you don't think you have done anything to make that person mad. Sometimes people are mean on a regular basis; and sometimes people are mean because they're having a really bad day and feel like they have to take it out on someone else. When people plan to bump into you, hurt you, or call you names to tease you or upset you, this is a bully.

It is tricky at times to figure out the difference between a bullying and a friendly or accidental bump because they all may feel the same. To truly decide the purpose of the bump, you have to "read" the person's intentions. One way to do this is to see the person's reaction after the two of you collide. If the person you collided with laughs and makes fun of you, his or her intention was likely to cause you harm on purpose. However, if the person bumps into you and immediately says "I'm sorry," "Excuse me," or "Are you okay?," he or she is letting you know it was an accident.

Avoid thinking that everyone who bumps into you is trying to cause you harm!! There are too many people moving around in a small space for us not to get accidentally bumped into every now and then! Realize, there are times when you bump into other people by accident. What do you do when this happens?

To Review:
THE LANGUAGE OF DIFFERENT BUMPS AND PUSHES *(and what your response should be)*:

1. **If you caused the accidental bump or push,** you immediately look at the person and say, "I am sorry." Offer to help the person back up to his feet or help to pick up something that he may have dropped.

2. **If she tripped while walking near you,** you immediately look at the person and then ask, "Are you all right?" Offer to help her back up to her feet or help to pick up something that she may have dropped.

3. **If someone else did an accidental bump or push** and says, "Excuse me," you can say, "It's all right," and just keep walking.

4. **If someone gave you a friendly bump or push,** then just laugh or smile and don't say anything to him (like words that you are mad that he touched you). The way you may figure out that it was a friendly bump is by remembering that this person has been truly nice to you in the past and is just showing you a middle-school, high-school aged way to be friendly.

5. **If someone gave you an unfriendly bump or push,** and you know this because he has not been genuinely nice to you in the past or tends to end up laughing at you or making fun of you, try not to say anything to him or to fight back. Instead go to an adult nearby and let her know what happened. If the same person keeps doing this to you, let the adult know this keeps happening and you need help with the situation. Students can also be bullied on the Internet; they don't have to just bump into you or tease you in person to be bullies. Make sure you talk to adults at your school and in your home if you suspect you're being bullied. Make sure you know the person's intentions are to cause you harm (hurt your feelings, make fun of you, make you scared). If the adult you're going to does not seem to be willing to help you, go talk to another adult. Talk to your parents about this as well. Bullies can be very tricky. They can act sweet to adults and mean to specific kids, so some adults don't believe that "such a nice kid" could be a bully!

If you continue to not be listened to, go to the principal, the principal's boss, etc. *Make sure you tell adults!!*

Making smart guesses about people you are with: *Are they friendly, bossy, or mean?*

How does their voice sound *(mean or friendly?)*

+ **What do they say to you? What words do they use?**

+ **What message does their body send?**

+ **What do you know about this person?**

+ **What is their plan?**

= _____

AFTER ADDING UP THE CLUES, YOU SHOULD BE ABLE TO COME UP WITH THE CORRECT ANSWER. FRIENDLY? BOSSY? OR MEAN?

Friendly Teasing and Mean Teasing

When we first think of the word "teasing," we think of something negative. However, as we develop relationships with others, one way that we may try to make a connection is by teasing others in a more friendly way. This type of teasing may show affection and be playful with those we like being around. Friendly teasing involves a lot of sarcasm. Sarcasm is when people joke with you by often telling you the opposite of what you expect them to say.

Here is an *example* of friendly teasing: Sarah and April are good friends. April tells Sarah she got an "A" on a test she'd been worried about. Sarah responds to April by saying, "That's too bad, your mom is going to be so mad!"

Give some *examples* of when a parent or friend used FRIENDLY TEASING or when you used friendly teasing.

1.

2.

3.

The tricky part of this is determining when someone may be teasing you in a *friendly* manner. Let's look at some ways to help you determine when someone might be doing that *friendly* thing:

- Does the person have a history of taking negative actions against you? *NO*
- Are you in a conflict with this person at the moment? *NO*
- Just before the action took place, was the person communicating in a negative way? *NO*
- Was this person trying to impress his friends or those around you? *NO*
- Did the person give you any nonverbal cues such as a smile or a smirk? *YES*
- Did the comment follow with a laugh or giggle? *YES*
- Did the person's tone sound friendly? *YES*
- Did the person stop when you asked for the teasing to stop? *YES*

If your answers match the ones listed above, it's very likely that *friendly teasing* was taking place. We respond to *friendly teasing* by just laughing or giving a smile.

Here's what you **DON'T** want to do:
Don't try to explain to the person why he's wrong! He already knows he was wrong; that was part of the joke.

Friendly teasing and sarcasm are really confusing, but they're also really popular strategies for maintaining a friendship. You may want to spend some extra time trying to observe how people use and interpret sarcasm by watching some sitcom-type TV shows that involve family and friend interactions. Virtually every comedy on TV that is a sitcom uses this type of humor heavily! It's best if you can watch these shows once they're recorded or on a DVD so that you can replay them and pause frequently.

You can also observe this at school, but it goes by so quickly it's difficult to study it in real time!

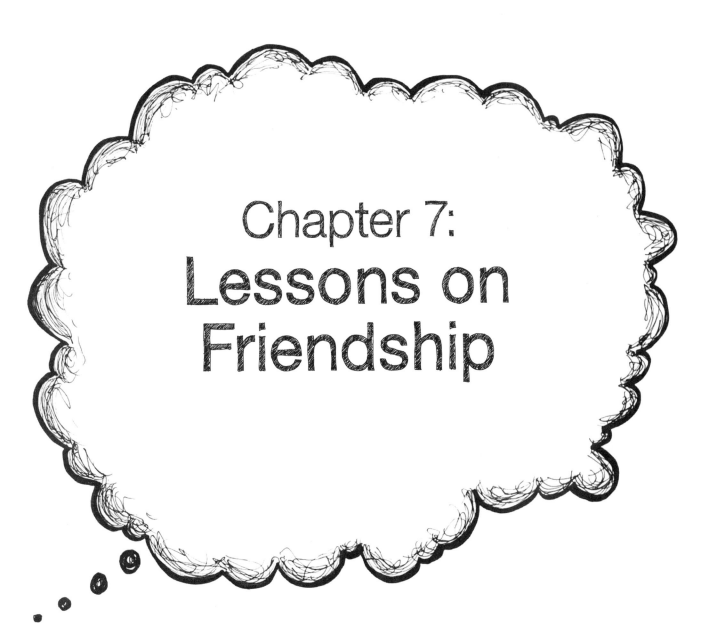

Chapter 7:
Lessons on
Friendship

Know the Difference Between:
Friends, Friendly Acquaintances, Others, and Mean People

Adults may tell you that you should call a friend or go hang out with your friends...but who really are friends?

Below we attempt to define this elusive or vague concept of how one person can be a friend to a few, a friendly acquaintance to many, mostly just an "other" to the masses. All of us once in awhile have to work to avoid either being a "mean person" or having to deal with mean others.

Think about the people you know and work on transforming friendly acquaintances into friends.

	Friends	Friendly Acquaintances	Others	Mean People
Who's Who?	People you choose to be your friend.	People who may cross your path and who are friendly to you when you see them.	People who may cross your path, but you just go about your day when around them. You don't greet or have a conversation with them.	People you really don't know but who seem to treat you poorly and make you feel bad when you're around them.
Having Conversations	You share secrets (trust).	You engage in more superficial conversation.	You don't talk to them because you don't know them.	You avoid talking to them.
How You Act Toward Them	You make an effort to locate them to spend more time with them.	You'll be friendly when you happen to be in the same place at the same time, but you don't seek them out.	You only notice them to avoid bumping into them when sharing space with them.	You avoid being near them.

	Friends	Friendly Acquaintances	Others	Mean People
What You Share	You share your thoughts and feelings with friends; you'll risk telling them more about how you feel than you would others.	Usually you don't tell them a lot about how you feel emotionally, *for example*, things bugging you or that you're super excited about.	No interaction usually.	No interaction if it can be avoided.
Communicating When Apart	You'll work to connect with them when you're apart (nights and weekends) by texting, emailing, phoning, or using Facebook. You'll also try to hang out with them during free time.	You don't work at communicating with them when away from them, but you might just run into them in regular places.	You don't work at communicating with them away from where you normally run into them.	You avoid.
Hanging Out	You can hang out with them happily without always talking...just hanging out in a comfortable way.	You only hang out with them if they happen to want to hang out with you or your friends.	You wouldn't hang out with them.	You avoid.

Progression of Levels of Friendship

Friends
- You often share something in common.
- They're people you can trust.
- They're people you feel comfortable being with.
- They're people you have experience with across time.
- Requires mutual agreement; both people have to agree to be friends with each other.

Identify where you are with various people you know. Review the different ways in which you can advance from one level to another.

Level 1 Friendly Greeting: Someone you're friendly to but really don't know, don't talk to, and don't hang out with at all.

  a. Say "Hi" to as many people as you're comfortable with greeting. However, if you notice you don't say "Hi" barely at all, identify one or two students to look for when you walk around and greet them when you see them (nonverbally or verbally).

  b. To greet people you don't have to actually say "hi"; you can just look in the direction of the people you want to greet and give them a little smile as you walk by them. That is interpreted as you "saying hi," even if you're not talking!

Level 2 Acquaintance: You have had some small discussions with these people usually because you worked with them in a classroom group or they're friends of a friend so you happened to hang out with them for a short while. You may look them up on Facebook even if you aren't their "friend" yet and ask if they want to be your friend.

  a. If there's someone who is always pretty friendly to you (says "hi" or acknowledges you in a positive way), when you see the person sitting in class sit near him or try to work together in a group during a classroom group activity.

  b. Someone just starts talking to you because you are physically near her (in line, sitting next to each other, etc.) and you respond to her comments or questions, showing an interest in her.

Level 3 Possible Friendship: This is when you start to seek out people to talk to them, but you meet up with them in the same general location that you met them. When you happen to see the person, ask to meet for lunch, break, or after school.

  a. Connect with the person using Facebook.
  b. Seek the person out to work with on a classroom project.
  c. Call or text the person about homework problems.
  d. Go up to the person when he or she is standing with another person, even if you don't know the other person.

Level 4 Evolving Friendship: This is when you are demonstrating to people that you would like to spend more time with them by trying to consistently hang out with them in school, work with them on projects, and most importantly contact them to see if they want to hang out outside of the place you met them. At this level you start to work at being friends by making plans with the person to do things later in the day or week, if the person chooses to be your friend as well.

   a.   Connect on Facebook and text.
   b.   Possibly call them with questions about your homework or other school events.
   c.   Hang out with them at school primarily.
   d.   If in your class, work with them on classroom projects.
   e.   Ask the person if he or she wants to get together to do something after school at your house or in the community (*for example, go to see a movie, etc.*).

Level 5 Bonded Friendship: This is when people are there for each other. They look out for each other and go out of their way to make sure things are okay for that person. It's expected you make plans to hang out with friends outside of more structured times (seeing them during the school day). This level represents that you are spending a lot of time with this person in the place you met them but also at home or in the community. It is similar to level 4, but just more intense.

   a.   Consistently seek out the person to hang out together, meeting him or her in the same place during lunch or break.
   b.   Post stuff on the person's Facebook wall, etc.
   c.   Arrange to talk or get together after school, just to hang out. What you do is NOT that important. It's being with someone that is more important.
   d.   Talk more personally about your life and your emotions with this person (what makes you frustrated, happy, and so on).

Level 6 Very Close Friendship: It's expected you do all the things in level 3 with this person but with a bit more intensity. It's expected you have some deeper conversations with this person when you need to do so. These are the folks you can really open up with. Not everyone has a really close friend, but they're worth having to give you someone else you talk to about feelings, worries, etc.

   a.   Hang out with the person frequently.
   b.   Definitely let him or her know when things are getting you down or what you are concerned about, but save these talks for when you are just with your close friends.
   c.   Your close friend will likely be friends with your bonded friends as well; it is just you feel a bit closer to this person than you do to your other bonded friends.
   d.   Your close friend will likely have other evolving or bonded friends that you don't know well. Be nice to his or her friends even if they're not your bonded friends. You treat your friend's friends well by showing an interest in them, etc.
   e.   You make a point of spending some part of your weekend time with this person.

On Again, Off Again Friendship: A special category into which many friendships fall is called *On Again, Off Again Friends*.

You will also find that many people with whom you have experienced level 3 to 6 friendship will also become "on again, off again" friends with you. This type of friendship is one that can be very nice, but the friendship doesn't last forever. It may only last for the period of time you share something in common such as going to the same school, being on the same team, in the same club, living on the same block, etc.

In truth, most friendships fall into this category; *for example*, you may be friends with someone for a semester, but once you don't have the same classes with that person you end up not hanging out with him or her so much. It's important to realize that most friendships may fade in and out or may move up and down across the levels of friendship. One friend may start as an acquaintance, quickly move up to a bonded friend, but then over time the friendship is no longer as strong. By the time you talk to the person again, you're almost back to just being acquaintances. This is to be expected and it is okay!

Avoid getting mad at the person if he or she "fades you out." We have many, many friends that will fade in and out of our lives at different times!

From Friendly to Friendship

A Friendship Peer-a-Mid

How different types of friendships develop

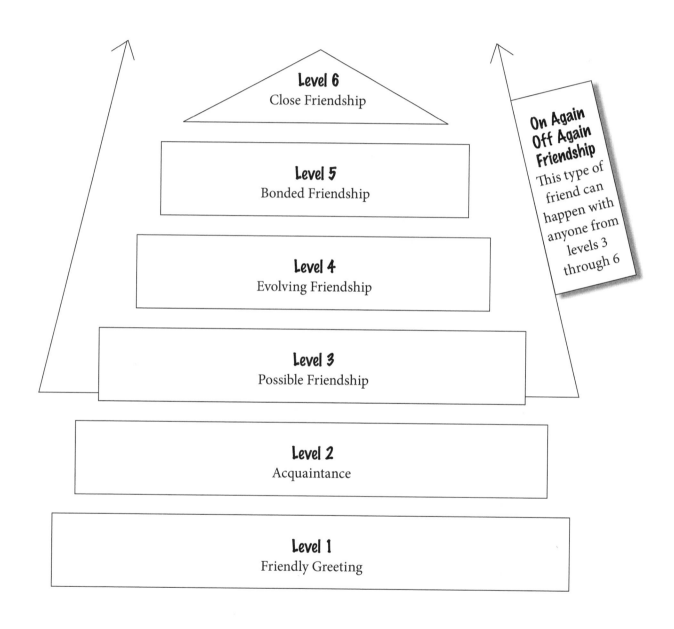

Level 6
Close Friendship

Level 5
Bonded Friendship

Level 4
Evolving Friendship

Level 3
Possible Friendship

Level 2
Acquaintance

Level 1
Friendly Greeting

On Again Off Again Friendship This type of friend can happen with anyone from levels 3 through 6

IF THERE IS BUT ONE LESSON...People will forget what you SAID...People will forget what you DID, BUT PEOPLE WILL NEVER FORGET HOW YOU MADE THEM FEEL...

-Anonymous

Friendly Is Not a Friendship, Yet

Being friendly simply contributes to people having positive thoughts about you. You can be friendly without having a friendship. This thinksheet focuses on what friendly is, why this is important for how people perceive you, and whether people will want to be your friend.

Define what you think of as someone being FRIENDLY.

Define what YOU do to be viewed as "friendly" by others when at school. Describe how facial expression and gestures contribute to this.

Define what you do to be thought of as "friendly" at home.

How do you feel when you don't view people as being friendly to you?

Is it possible to be too friendly? Describe what this might look like. How do people feel if you're too friendly?

We know it's possible to be unfriendly. What makes you act unfriendly?

How do the rules of friendliness change in different situations?

For example, compare what's friendly in different places. Consider the following: humor, physical approach and actions, length of talking time, smiles, topic selection, swearing, and so on.

What are the subtle or not so subtle differences? What are the reasons for these differences?

Friendly at Lunchtime at School	Friendly at School	Friendly at Home

FRIEND or DNEIRF?

A friend is someone who shows that he or she enjoys being around you and shows you this by doing nice things with and for you. Someone who doesn't care about others while hanging out together, we can call a DNEIRF (friend spelled backwards)!! Let's think about what it takes to be a friend and some of the ways someone might be a DNEIRF.

When might we need to be a friend? Is it just when we are hanging out or playing a game?

What does a FRIEND say or do?	What does a DNEIRF say or do?
Keeps body in the group	Gets into others' personal space
Uses friendly words	Is bossy or rude to others
Keeps thinking about what the group is doing	Only wants to do what he or she wants to do
Is a good sport/is flexible about winning, losing, and the use of his or her ideas	Is a poor sport/argues
Shares	Says mean words
Thinks of others' plans	Doesn't share
Honors others' thoughts by agreeing or nicely saying why it might not work	Hits
Listens to others' suggestions and ideas by looking toward them	Loses control with his or her body or words!
Nods his or her head or says a word that tells the other person that he or she is listening, communicating "good idea"	Yells
	Grabs things from others
	Disrespects others' thoughts by saying things like, "That's not a good idea, my idea is better..."
	Doesn't respond to someone else's idea

Being a Guest

As you prepare for a day as someone's guest, it's important to remember the IMPRESSIONS we make. There are certain GUESTLY behaviors that are expected when we visit someone else's home. Alex Packer, in his book **How Rude!** (1997), reviews tips for being a good guest. We have listed many of his ideas and added some of our own below. Let's discuss them.

1. BE ON TIME—You've agreed to visit this person, and to not show up would be rude. Maybe this person (or his or her parent) has done a lot of planning for the big day. What could you do if you're running late?

2. DON'T BE TOO EARLY—Usually the host is trying to get things done and that might make it difficult if you show up early. What could you do if you do arrive early?

3. DON'T BRING OVER PEOPLE WHO WERE NOT INVITED—Why not?

4. DON'T BE A FOOD HOG—The food is usually out for everyone to enjoy so you should try to leave some for everyone, even if the food is really good.

5. DO YOUR BEST TO BE CHEERFUL—All of us have bad days, and you may even have a bad day the day you said you'd go over to someone's house. It's not great to hold in your feelings, but it's also not a great idea to bring the mood down while at someone's house. Sometimes we have to just FAKE IT! What could you do if this happens to you?

6. DO WHAT YOUR FRIEND IS DOING—If you're at a friend's house, you want to try to show that you're thinking about him or her. One way to do this is by doing what your friend does. For example, if he or she goes into the other room to watch TV, you go with. Or if your friend is playing video games, you play video games with him or her. How does it feel to someone when he or she has invited you over and you're not even doing the same thing together?

7. DON'T FORGET YOUR MANNERS—Remember to say "please" and "thank you," and use table manners if you sit down for a meal. What are some table manners?

    a._____

    _____

    b._____

    _____

    c._____

    _____

8. USE YOUR EYES TO LOOK FOR CLUES.

  a. Look for any clues that your friend might be getting bored with the activity you're doing together. If this happens, you may want to suggest something else to do or find out what your friend would like to do. What might this look or sound like?

  b. Look for any clues that your friend might give you if it's getting too late for him or her. What might this look or sound like?

9. THANK YOUR FRIEND AND SAY IT LIKE YOU MEAN IT!

10. DON'T FORGET TO SAY GOODBYE—What are some cool ways to say goodbye?

. . . .

THE HOST

You, the HOST, have a lot of responsibilities to your guest as well!

1. Review the guidelines for being a Guest, because most of them apply to you as the host as well!

2. SEE THAT EVERYONE IS HAVING A GOOD TIME—Friends will give you clues if they're uncomfortable with something or if they're bored with something you're doing together...so BE AWARE!

3. IF YOU'RE EATING A MEAL, OFFER YOUR GUESTS FOOD AND DRINKS—You want to show them that you're thinking about them by letting them eat first. Also, if you start to run out of food, you, and not your guest, will have to eat something else.

4. IF YOU DON'T HAVE A MEAL PLANNED—Occasionally ask your friends if they'd like anything to eat or drink, especially if they've been at your house for awhile.

How Rude! By Alex J Packer, Ph.D.

What Can You Expect?

	Girlfriend/Boyfriend or Girl/Guy You Like	Best Friend	Friend	Acquaintance/ Classmate
	Different Expectations for Different People in Your Life			
Greetings	Hug/kiss/say hello	What's up? Cool handshake Hi	What's up?	What's up? Hi
Topics	Their interests Similar interests	Their interests Similar interests	Their interests Similar interests	School-related topics, tests, assignments, projects
Planned Activities **Places to Go with Them**	Movies Restaurants	Movies Restaurants Sleepover with same sex friend Hang out at home	Hang out at home, school Sports Dances	Probably only talk to them where you usually see them (for example, at school, church, etc.)
	Jerk/Bully	**Stranger**	**Adult You Know**	**Adult You Don't Know**
Greetings	Ignore	Hi Or ignore	Hi, Mr. _____ Hi	Hi, Mr. _____ Handshake
Topics	Ignore	Small talk trying to find common interests	Small talk trying to find common interests	Small talk trying to find common interests
Planned Activities or Places to Go with Them	None	None	None unless they're accompanying a group on an outing (as the driver, for example)	None

154

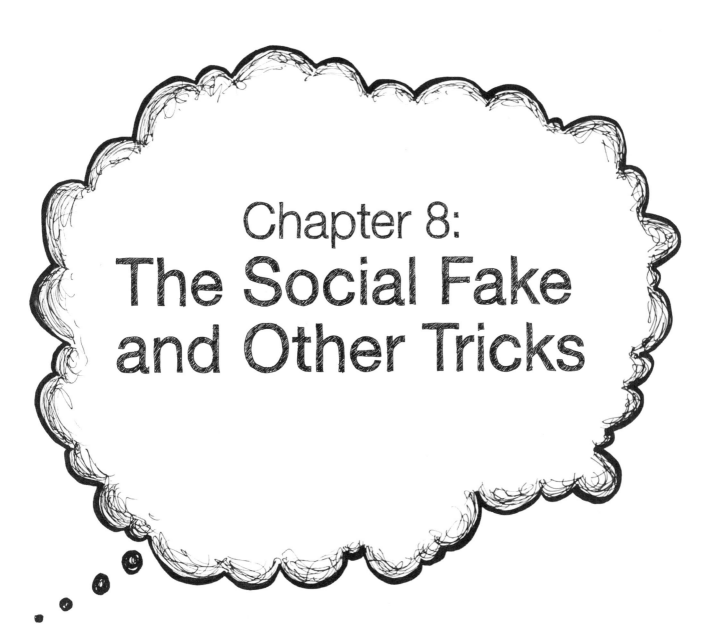

Chapter 8:
The Social Fake
and Other Tricks

I'm Not Interested in What You're Saying

The ultimate SOCIAL FAKE is to be able to listen to someone talk about something that you're not interested in but come across to the person as if you ARE interested! At some point, most conversations become a little bit boring. When this happens, instead of telling people they're boring us, we just fake it! We act like we're interested even if we're not. You may not realize it, but people use the social fake with you at times. Not everything anyone says is interesting all the time. So because people do the social fake with you, you should learn to do it with others as well. It's a little thing we all learn to do to help us stay calm when we hang out and talk to each other.

List *three* types of choices you have when a conversation you're having has become boring:

A Bad Choice	A Good Choice	A Good Choice

What makes the bad choice of how to handle your boredom that you listed a bad choice?

_____

_____

To do the good choices, what do you have to do with your body so that you're really "FAKING IT WITH SUCCESS"?

_____

_____

What does it mean to "FAKE IT WITH SUCCESS"?

_____

_____

Social Fake

Sometimes people talk about topics that I'm not really interested in. During these times, I can show the other people that I care about them by listening anyway. When I "pretend" to be interested in what someone is saying (even though I'm not), I'm doing the "Social Fake"! People feel happy when we listen to them and when we're interested in what they have to say. You never know...they just might say something I find interesting after all.

· ·

To do the Social Fake:

1. Look at the person who is talking.

2. Match my facial expressions to the message.

3. Make positive comments and ask questions that will keep the conversation going.

· ·

This week I'll practice the Social Fake during dinnertime. When family members talk about something that doesn't interest me much, I'll listen and pretend to be interested. I'll ask questions and make positive comments because it's fun to join in, and it will let my family know that I care about them. They'll feel happy and proud that I'm joining in! (They'll have good thoughts about me.)

Put a *checkmark* in the box each day that you did "THE SOCIAL FAKE."

Monday	Tuesday	Wednesday	Thursday	Friday	Saturday	Sunday

© 2011 Think Social Publishing, Inc. • www.socialthinking.com

The Steps of the Social Fake

1. LOOK at the person.

    a. Turn your body toward the person.
    b. Look at the person's face.

2. LISTEN to the person.

3. Make comments about what the person is talking about to keep the conversation going.

4. ASK QUESTIONS about what the other person is talking about.

5. Match your EXPRESSION to the message.

6. SHOW INTEREST in someone else's area of interest to keep that person feeling good and to create a positive impression.

The Social Fake When You Receive a Gift That Doesn't Thrill You

Another time we need to do the social fake is when we receive presents from others that we don't particularly like. *For example*, let's pretend Aunt Bessie comes to your house over the holidays and gives you socks. But you don't really like to get socks as a present! You'd rather get a Game Boy™ or a video game.

You might even feel disappointed that you got socks instead of a "cool" gift. But this is the time to think more about your aunt's feelings than your own feelings. This is when you need to show your aunt that you care about her by doing the Social Fake. If you look sad or disappointed, or if you say "I hate socks, I wanted a Game Boy," your aunt will feel sad and might even have "weird thoughts" about you.

Remember! It's important to think about others' feelings and to keep your feelings of disappointment inside. People feel happy when we show them we care about them and this causes them to have great thoughts about us. There are times we need to tell the truth to people, but we are expected to do it in a way that doesn't hurt their feelings.

. . . .

To do the Social Fake when you get a present that you didn't really want:

1. **Look at the person.**

2. **Keep your sad or disappointed feelings inside.**

3. **Show that you're happy that the person cares about you.**

4. **Say, "Thank you."**

How did you do? Did you do the Social Fake when you got a present that you didn't really want?

Figurative Language = Figure-It-Out Language

Our language can be kind of tricky. It can be tricky because sometimes the words you hear or read may mean something completely different than what you thought the words meant. This is called "figurative language." When we hear it or read it, we have to make guesses to understand it. WE NEED TO FIGURE IT OUT! What happens if we're not very good at figuring out the different meanings in our language when we talk to others?

In class?

_____

_____

In stories or textbooks?

_____

_____

Let's have some fun and look at sentences to try to figure out what the words are saying. These expressions are called "idioms."

	Literal Meaning	Figurative Meaning *(Figure it out)*
Our neighbors are *nosy*.		
I am *in a pickle*.		
That math homework was *a piece of cake*.		

Indirect Language: What Does It Really Mean?

Teachers, parents, and friends often say things that imply or suggest what they mean—they don't say exactly what they mean. This is part of figurative language as well because your brain has to figure it out!

Often in American culture, when people use direct language it is often interpreted that they are angry!

Below is a chart that explores indirect language and what it literally means.

Indirect language or humor	Direct, literal meaning of the words or phrases
Listen up.	Be quiet now! or Shut up!
I'll take care of that.	Don't touch it, I want to do it.
"Thank you" as a response to an answer you provided in class.	Means...Your turn is done. Do not keep talking.
Time to work.	Get out your materials, get your body into your chair, and don't talk to others.
This is a good time to turn it in.	Turn it in now.
Knock it off.	Stop whatever you're doing that's making someone frustrated.
It would be great if you guys discussed this topic...	Please stop talking about other things and stay on task.
How about if you get your binder organized? or It would be nice if you got your binder organized right now.	Take the time to do it now, and don't do anything else.
Why don't you guys work on your own?	Stop talking and looking at each other's papers.
We have this paper to study for...(as you approach a group).	You are not welcome in the group.
If you have a moment, why don't you set the table (at home)?	Please set the table now.

© 2011 Think Social Publishing, Inc. • www.socialthinking.com

Indirect language or humor	Direct, literal meaning of the words or phrases
I am really busy.	I don't have time to talk to you.
You guys are really bothering me.	Change your behavior.
I am not having a good day. or Life sucks.	Be nice to me.
You are such a loser. You're a nerd. I hate you! etc.	Some indirect expressions are forms of sarcasm and you can only tell what they mean based on how close you are to that person. These phrases can be expressions of close friendships...though if you don't know the person well, she may say it with a smile, but she may really mean it!
In a minute. Just a second.	Not right now—I need some time to finish (*a thought or activity*).
Can you think of more?	

Things to do with this:

1. Talk to parents, teachers, and friends about how they feel when the language is stated directly versus indirectly.

2. Try using some of these indirect terms and see if you notice people treating you a bit more calmly.

3. Notice how others, such as your teachers and family, use these types of language. Try to figure out why they choose to use indirect language rather than direct language. Direct language is usually a faster way to communicate, so why don't we all just choose to tell people exactly what we think? (*Tip: It has to do with how the words make other people feel!*)

Are Your Intentions Honorable?

When you hear someone talk about another person's *intentions*, it means they were trying to figure out how the person was planning to treat another person. If you hear someone say, "Did Cheryl *intend* to do that to you?," it means they were questioning if Cheryl had planned in advance to treat you the way she did. Or, if someone says, "I think Cheryl had good intentions, even if you got upset," that means Cheryl was probably trying to do something that made you feel good, but it backfired (her plan did not work).

When you are around others, they think about you and you think about them. All people also make plans in their head (form intentions) about what they want to do with someone. Unfortunately, not all plans (intentions) are good (honorable). Some people have intentions to make others feel embarrassed or sad.

When people have bad intentions, they may try and trick us in a mean way. They might pretend to be a friend when really they're just trying to bully us into doing things we know are not okay!

The weird thing is that sometimes people also trick us when they want to be playful or friendly. *Tricking another person is not always filled with bad intentions!*

Sometimes it's confusing to try to figure out if someone was teasing us in fun or if they were really being mean. There are some clues to look for to determine if someone is trying to be mean to you (has bad intentions) or if the person is just trying to be playful (has good intentions).

1. Probably the most important thing to consider is: "What do I know about the person who is trying to trick me?"

    a. Has he been nice to me previously? (*If he has been nice to you on most occasions, there is a good chance he has good intentions when he tricks you.*)

    b. Is she only nice to me when it is just the two of us, but she makes me feel upset once she gets into groups with others? (*This type of person may be trying to show off to friends and does not have good intentions.*)

    c. Is he always mean to me? (*You know this person doesn't have good intentions toward you; he never does!*)

    d. Does she usually ignore me? (*You would then wonder why she is paying attention to you now. That makes you question the person's intentions even more!*)

2. Other ways to try and figure out another kid's intentions are by:

    a. Listening to his tone of voice. (*Does he sound mean or angry?*)

    b. Looking at her facial expression. (*Does it look mean or angry?*)

c. Is he looking at the other kids around him and laughing or smiling while he tricks me? (*This usually means he's trying to show off to them by making you feel bad...which means he has bad intentions.*)

d. Does she only do what she is doing to me when no adult is around?

e. Once he tricks me does he quickly leave me alone, laughing? (*This means he probably has the bad intention of making fun of you.*)

f. Once she tricks me does she stick by me and start to talk to me in a friendly way? (*This means she likely has good intentions and just wanted to play around or joke with you.*)

g. Some other ways I can do this as well are:

Can you remember different situations when people treated you in a way that made you question if they had good or bad intentions?

_____

_____

_____

_____

If so, describe what happened and explain why they made you think their intentions were good or bad.

_____

_____

_____

_____

_____

Exploring Lying

People use many different reasons for lying. *Some of the reasons are:*

1. To protect yourself from getting in trouble.
2. To avoid having to do certain things.
3. To make other people feel good.

Can you think of another reason?

Now let's think about the different types of lies.

1. Protecting yourself from getting in trouble. What do these types of lies sound like?

    a.

    b.

    c.

    d.

    e.

What do these lies look like if we draw people's thoughts?

2. Lies that help you to avoid having to do something.

    a.

    b.

    c.

    d.

    e.

Make a comic strip conversation and write in their thoughts:

Lying to protect yourself or to get things you want are called **BAD LIES** because they make people have bad thoughts about you!

3. Surprisingly, there are also "white lies," which are lies that people tell to make others feel good. *Some examples of good lies are:*

    a.   Sample: A friend gets a haircut and you don't really like it. Your friend then says, "How do you like my haircut?" When telling a "white lie," you may say, "It looks good!"

    b.

    c.

    d.

    e.

What do good lies look like? *(Use pictures of people's thoughts.)*

When people figure out you're telling Bad Lies, how do they feel about you? Make a Social Behavior map to explore what happens.

Honesty

What does it mean to be honest?_____

_____

Telling the truth when you did something wrong can be tough, but why is it important that you tell the truth?

_____

_____

> ### Tell about a time when you were honest and told the truth.

How does being honest show others you're thinking about them?

Why is it important to be honest?

1.

2.

3.

Honesty builds trust with others and makes people have good thoughts about you.

Are there times when we can be too honest...and hurt someone's feelings?

> ### Tell a time when someone was too honest to you and hurt your feelings.

Let's ACT OUT some situations and look at the impressions people make when they're not being honest.

Truth or Not the Truth?

Topic	Truth	White Lie	Bold-Faced Lie
Someone has asked you how their new shoes look. *(The shoes are a little outdated.)*			
What type of grade are you getting in Math?			
Did you do your homework for today? *(Let's assume you did it!)*			
Someone asks you to go somewhere and you don't want to go.			
Someone asks you about what you want to do when you get older.			

Chapter 9:
Participating
in Groups

Classroom Discussions:
Maintain a Topic, Talk Briefly, and Avoid the Tangent!

When a teacher directs a discussion, students are expected to stay on the same topic as the teacher. Questions to ask should directly relate to what the teacher is encouraging the class to talk about. This is what's meant by "maintaining a topic."

You can ask questions or make comments that help to add new information to a topic or to show the teacher that you've been studying the assigned materials.

Ask questions or make comments that are brief in length!

It's really important to keep your comments and questions short so that your thoughts don't take up too much of the whole class time. A short comment or question is one that can be stated within about 5–10 seconds!

Watch your peers in class, and you'll see that most offer short to-the-point comments or questions that demonstrate they're connecting to what the teacher is teaching. They don't try to dominate the talking time in class.

Remember that the teacher has to try and encourage every student in the class to participate. That means that there may be 30 students who need a little bit of time to ask a question or make a comment.

Using "WH-" and "How" Questions to Direct Comments and Questions

To consider what types of information may be helpful to add to a class discussion, think about the "WH-" and "How" questions: What, Where, How, Who, and Why.

Here are some different ways we use "WH-" and "How" questions and comments to join classroom discussions. This is not a complete list; it's just to get you started thinking about this!

WHAT

- WHAT is the topic? What are we supposed to be focused on related to the topic?
- WHAT does the teacher assume we already know?
- WHAT new information does she want us to learn?
- WHAT don't I understand?

HOW

- HOW is my question important for me to learn more about this topic? HOW is my comment important to demonstrate I've read the assignment or done my homework? How will my question affect the group that listens to it? Will they think I am still on the same topic as them or that I wasn't listening to what was discussed earlier?

- We might want to ask HOW something happened.

- We might also want to ask a question about HOW something works that relates to the specific topic being discussed.

- If you do know HOW something works, be careful not to share too much information about what you know with your class unless they specifically ask for this information. Talking too much to the class about all you know can make you appear as a "show-off."

WHEN

For subjects such as history or language arts, we may need to know WHEN something happened in history or when something happened to a character in a book. Comments or questions related to WHEN can be important because they help us understand the flow of events. What happens first often kicks off what happens next in a story or history, so it is important to know the order in which events happen.

WHERE

In class, WHERE questions are often asked about where to put something, such as WHERE to turn in our homework! We also ask WHERE questions about the location of a specific event being discussed or about the setting for a book. Where things happen is important because the setting (location) often suggests to us the hidden rules for how people are supposed to behave based on that specific location.

WHO

- If the class is studying individuals or groups of people, WHO are the people we need to know about?

- WHO is a person I have learned about that I can comment on to add to the discussion?

WHY

- WHY questions relate to providing a more detailed explanation about WHY an event happened the way it did, WHY a certain math equation turns out the way it does, and so on.

- If the teacher asks a WHY question to the students, you can answer with a comment or explanation. However, try and limit the length of your answer to no more than 10 seconds.

Avoid tangent talking!

By middle school, teachers usually discourage discussions that relate an academic topic to students' personal experiences. *For example*, if the teacher is discussing Roman history and you've been to Rome, it's unlikely the teacher or class wants to hear about your trip. This is called "going off on a tangent." A tangent is when you state out loud your thoughts that are in some way related to the topic but that do not directly stay on the current topic. Talking about a family's trip to Rome, Italy is not directly related to Roman history, so it's a *tangent*.

Teachers find it difficult to teach, and students find it difficult to learn when a member of the class states a lot of information that is a tangent or tangential because it distracts from the direct lessons that need to be explored. Distractions cause both the teacher and fellow students to feel a little frustrated when they observe that one member of the class is struggling to think about the purpose of the group discussion.

Asking Questions When You're Part of a Classroom Group

We're often in groups with other students and a teacher. Can you name some different places you go when you're in a group with a teacher?

Usually these groups have many students and only one teacher. Many kids are eager to learn and have lots of questions for the teacher about what they're learning. It makes it hard for a teacher to teach the class if all of the students or even just one student asks a lot of questions. Many times it's important for students to listen to the teacher, because he has a plan for the group. As he teaches, some of those questions you have in your head may get answered.

. . . .

Here are some steps to take if you feel you have an *important question* to ask:

1. I need to remember that the questions that students ask the teacher should relate to the topic and be helpful for the other kids as well. Sometimes the teacher may call on me and then it will be my turn to talk.

2. It's important for me to remember to not ask TOO MANY questions during the group because this can disrupt the group, and the teacher may feel worried that she isn't able to teach her students.

3. To ask a question, I can quietly raise my hand and look toward the teacher and wait for her to call on me.

4. When I'm in a group, I'll try to ask only a few *(one to three)* important questions so the teacher can keep teaching! If I have more questions, I can wait until after class and see if my teacher has time to answer another question. It will please my teacher if I can learn to ask only a few questions while in the group. It will also make the other students feel happy, because they'll get to keep learning from the teacher and can ask questions they have.

When Joining a Group to Hang Out and Talk, Use the SLOW APPROACH!

Sometimes a person comes up to a group of other people and just starts talking. The person POUNCES on or bombards the people in the group with questions or comments. The others may feel overwhelmed or irritated and may even snap in response (show frustration with words). Here's what happens in the POUNCE: You walk up to someone and you start talking to him without first showing you're thinking about him or paying attention to what he is saying or who he is saying it to.

When we use the SLOW APPROACH, we show others we're thinking about them. They'll then respond more positively to us. Here's how to do the SLOW APPROACH: When you approach someone, you first need to THINK about that person. You need to LOOK at the person and silently ask yourself, "What is she doing right now? Is this a good time to talk with her?" If you decide that this is a good time to talk with her, you can then move your body closer to her to set up your physical presence (but not too close). You need to keep looking at the person and thinking about her until she looks back at you. That tells you she's ready to listen. Then, finally, you add your words.

How do you know if people think you Pounce or do the Slow Approach?

One of the most difficult things we do as communicators is try to observe how people perceive us as we attempt to hang out or talk to them. Pay attention to how others see your behavior. Do they see you as Pouncing or using the Slow Approach?

When observing how people see you in their own eyes, realize that how you wish you are perceived may not be how you are actually perceived. Work at observing how others observe you. This is an important thing to be able to do because then you can make some smart guesses about how people feel about you and why.

And remember…this is something that's difficult for everyone to do!

Here are some tips for how to use the Slow Approach:

1. **Think about the person by looking at him and thinking about him:** What is he doing? Is this a good time to talk with him? If you're unsure, ask if this is a good time to talk.

2. **Move your body into position.**

3. **Look at the person:** How soon should you start to look at him? ANSWER: From before you start talking to him and then on and off until after you "close the conversation" with him.

4. **Add your own thoughts when they relate to what someone else is saying.** Try to avoid adding thoughts that don't seem to connect to what other people are discussing.

5. **Close the conversation** by saying something like "I gotta go," "See ya later," or "Bye."

As much as it is usually wise to use the *Slow Approach*, sometimes it's okay to *Pounce*. This is almost always when there's an emergency to report or you have quickly joined a group to give someone a quick message. When you *Pounce* (enter the group quickly and give your message), you are also supposed to leave the group just as quickly. You can't usually *Pounce* and then join the group and hang out.

How did you do this week practicing the SLOW APPROACH?

	Monday	Tuesday	Wednesday	Thursday	Friday	Saturday	Sunday
I did a great job!							
I did a so-so job.							
Oops! I need to work harder! I caught myself *Pouncing* too often.							

Hanging Out: Being Perceived as Friendly, Cooperative, and Approachable

Friendly people are those who are perceived to work well with other people. People like it when other people work well with them. Good players, folks who are perceived as cooperative, don't just play well during sports or other games; they also work well with other people at home, in the classroom during group project time, or even while waiting their turn at their desk. People who hang out well can stand in a group with others and not have the focus of attention be all about them all of the time.

When we're considered to be friendly or "approachable," the reward is that people enjoy spending time with us.

Here are some *ideas* for how to be considered *cooperative, approachable, friendly*:

1. **Move your body to go where the group goes.** Sometimes these are big movements like walking across the schoolyard; at other times, they're small movements, like just moving your shoulders to stay with the group.

2. **Think with your eyes.** Stay alert to watching what people are doing, what they might be feeling, and where they might be looking!

3. **Think about the people you're with.** What do they want from you? How do they feel when they're in the group? How should your body be turned when you're with them to encourage them to include you in the group?

4. **If it's a little boring for you but appears to be fun for the other person, you'll stay with the group…**because you know that when the group is doing or talking about something you think is cool, it might be a little boring for another person. Not everyone in the group enjoys all the same things all the time!

5. **No one knows it all!** Being part of a group means not telling people everything you know. People want to work or hang out with you—not just learn from you! Sometimes people actually get mad if someone else always tries to tell them things. That's because they feel like the person is acting like a "know-it-all." Being a "know-it-all" is not a good thing.

6. **All people keep learning to be cooperate, hang out, and be friendly across their lives!** Being "friendly" takes a lot of thinking, hanging out, and engaging in activities together to allow for practice to get it right! Keep trying to spend some time with other kids your age. This gives you some practice time to figure out how to think about what others think and feel. It also gives them a chance to see a really good side of you! Remember, everyone is learning social participation, not just you!

What to Talk About When Hanging Out with Others: Ideas for Conversation Starters

Memories shared with a specific person: Can be about a person you went to school with together An event at school Talking about someone you both know A place you have both been, even if you weren't there together A story, TV show, or movie you have both watched **	**What are your memories?**
General seasonal topics: Plans for upcoming holidays Plans for upcoming seasons (summer vacations, snow trips, etc.) Elections	**What topics can you think of?**
News events of interest: Earthquakes, big sports events, concerts, etc. Recent local events you saw on TV or read about on the Internet.	**What news events can you think of?**
Specific enjoyable experiences that you can share: Books you've read Places you've gone Things you saw during your day (a traffic accident, a funny photograph) Something you heard someone say that struck you as intelligent, stupid, etc. Passing on a story you heard of interest Many other things...	**What are experiences that you can talk about?**
Other topics?	**What topics can you provide information about?**

** Part of the reason to go to movies, watch TV shows, and so on is to keep on top of what other people may also experience. This gives you more opportunities to relate to them.

RULES for LIFE

Rules for being part of ANY group:

1. Pay attention to the group. This means listen to others' words and look at the face of the speaker and others nearby who are also in the group.
2. Keep your body in the group, with shoulders facing the group.
3. Add your thoughts, comments, and questions to the group!

Rules for being part of a group WHEN THINGS DON'T TURN OUT THE WAY YOU WANT! When things don't turn out the way we want, we all feel any number of emotions that might include feeling frustrated, annoyed, angry, mad, sad, disappointed, stressed, furious, etc. Even when we feel this way, other members of the group still expect certain behaviors from us.

Behaviors that are EXPECTED, even if you're upset, include:

- A sad face
- Words of disappointment like "darn" or "shoot"
- A steady voice that is not loud
- A chance to explain. (You may get a chance to explain why you feel upset. At other times, you don't need to explain; it's just what you have to put up with. *For example*, if someone else gets to go first, you don't need to explain why you're upset. However, if you lost your favorite pen, you may need to explain this because no one knows why you're sad.)

When you do *expected* behaviors, even when you're upset or sad, other people stay calm and are more willing to help you.

Behaviors that are UNEXPECTED, even if you're upset, include:

- An angry face
- Yelling out your thoughts about why you're mad
- Telling people how much you hate them
- Big gestures that show people that your body is going out of control
- Running away or hiding
- Refusing to do any more work
- Insisting things have to go your way
- Hitting
- Saying bad words

When you do these unexpected behaviors, it makes other people feel angry or sad themselves. When they feel this way, it's hard for them to treat you well during that time.

We know things won't all go well each day. So each day we get to practice trying to keep our behaviors to what others expect, so that they can continue to work with us and help us.

Fitting In: Developing an Awareness of the Impressions We Have of Each Other

Making impressions at school: Whether we like to admit it or not, people think about each other when they share space together. While we each want to be thought of as a unique individual, weirdly our uniqueness seems to be more desired when we also try and fit in.

Fitting in means that we are aware of others' expectations and adapt some of our behaviors to meet some of those social expectations.

From about fourth grade through high school, kids tend to be highly aware of what others wear, how they wear it, hygiene, etc.

Be aware, others will have thoughts and even judgments based on how you show up at school, even when you're not talking to anyone else. They'll still observe you and have thoughts about you (just like you do about them).

Defining Impressions in Three Ways:

1. How You Look

- People think about your hair. Is it clean? Do you have dandruff? Do you cut or style your hair in a way that's similar to other kids your age?

- Are your clothes similar to those worn by other kids your age? What you choose to wear should vary throughout your life and somewhat match what other kids your age wear. *For example*, when you were eight years old, it was very cool to wear a Pokeman® t-shirt to school, but it is totally NOT cool to wear this in middle school.

- Adults may not be that "tuned in" to the clothes or hairstyles of middle school kids that make a positive impression on others, so you have to be your own detective on this.

- Adults are usually "tuned in" to hygiene. They probably understand more than kids the importance of keeping your body, teeth, hair, and clothes clean, not just to make a good impression but to help keep you healthy!

2. What You Say

- People hear the words you say and try to guess what you're trying to communicate. For example, if you say "hi" but use an angry tone of voice, people will think you're being mean or sarcastic.

- By the time you were in third grade, you had to be careful not to talk too much about what you know. If a teacher asks a student to answer a question and the student tells everything she knows about the topic, other classmates who also hear the answer can become annoyed. If you're not sure how much information is requested, give short answers of only a few sentences. If the teacher wants you to explain more, she'll ask.

- People often interpret whether you're friendly in part by how you use your language. Greeting people, even if it's a quick "Hi" or "What's up?," demonstrates to others that you're acknowledging them!

- *Small talk* is important; it's a way to connect with people. It's not "smart talk"; a person isn't supposed to show people all they know when having a short conversation with another person. Instead, small talk involves asking other people questions about things like their day, their classes, or their weekend plans to show you're interested in the other person. By asking someone a question about what he thinks about something, you give him an opportunity to ask you a similar question or for you to find what things you might enjoy doing together.

- In classrooms, teachers prefer you keep your social talk to a minimum, even though they still want you to be friendly. Teachers expect you to be friendly by showing you're interested in them and the other members of your class in a positive way.

3. What You Do

- We're most often around people when we're NOT talking. That means we keep an eye on (observe) what others do when they're near us. People feel the calmest around people who do what's expected for different situations. For example, if you sit and listen to a teacher talk by looking at the teacher and keeping your hands on your desk and body turned toward the teacher, everyone will have a normal thought about you as a member of a class. However, if you start to pick your nose while your body and eyes are turned toward the teacher, people start to have more of a weird thought (bad impression).

- When people have made an impression on you, you tend to remember how they made you feel. How we think about someone based on how they look, what they say, and what they do affects how we feel about them. Our feelings tend to go into our social memory, and we tend to remember people once we start thinking about them.

- Observe the memories you have about people in your class.

  1. Think of three people you've spoken to in your class and describe the types of social memories you have of that person.

  2. Now think of three people in your class you've never spoken to but that you realize you have social memories about as well. Why do you have those memories? How does your memory of them affect whether you want to talk or work with them in the future?

  3. Our social memories of people help us to create people files in our brains where we store memories of specific people and then decide if we want to be with that person in the future!

Lesson on the three parts of making an impression is adapted from *Social Skill Strategies: A Social-Emotional Curriculum for Adolescents,* Book A, pages 116-121 (Gajewski, Hirn, and Mayo, 1998).

Staying Connected to the Group

It's your job to practice staying connected to the group with your brain, body, eyes, and words. How did you do staying connected today? *Rate yourself 1–5. A 5 means you did great and a 1 means you need lots of practice.*

1. **I shared my ideas with the group.**

   1   2   3   4   5

2. **I listened to other people's ideas and gave them feedback.**

   1   2   3   4   5

3. **I stayed connected to the group with my eyes and body.**

   1   2   3   4   5

4. **If I got distracted, I was able to focus again on the group without someone else reminding me.**

   1   2   3   4   5

A strength of mine today was:

_____

_____

_____

Something I need to practice is:

_____

_____

_____

Working Effectively with Others

Over the next few weeks, we'll plan and organize an outing together. This isn't an easy task. It's helpful to be familiar with some group concepts that help a group move forward and make decisions.

Communicate

. . . .

Using the four steps of communication, how do we communicate? *How do we use our:*

Thinking:

Body proximity and presence:

Eyes:

Words:

Participate

. . . .

How often do we participate?

Can we over-participate? Under-participate?

What are the expectations of a leader?

What are the expectations of those not chosen to be the leader?

Social Thinking® Thinksheets for Tweens and Teens   © 2011 Think Social Publishing, Inc. • www.socialthinking.com

Negotiate

. . . .

Give an example of negotiating:

What could we say to negotiate? What tone should we use?

1.

2.

Compromise

. . . .

Give an example of compromising:

What could we say? What tone should we use?

What does it mean to go with the majority vote? What does this look and sound like?

Keeping the Group Together

We have been working on learning to think about others. One way we do this is by exploring our emotions and trying to get more control over them. Our emotions are CONTAGIOUS AND THEY CAN SPREAD. If we're really mad it can change how everyone feels in the group about us. This is an important concept for everyone in this group if we want to:

- Be a better problem solver
- Be a better social thinker so that we keep making good impressions and so that others want to keep hanging around us
- Feel good and proud of ourselves!

To do this, we have been learning how to: 1) Think about how our actions make people feel so that we keep them feeling good about us and not angry! 2) Control our own anger and try to respond more in a more expected manner so we keep making a pretty good impression and ultimately feel better about ourselves! Let's take a closer look at what you can do to keep the group functioning.

1. One thing I can try to change when I am around _____is_____

_____. This will keep him or her feeling happy and wanting to be a part of the group.

2. One thing I can keep doing when I am around _____is_____

_____. This will keep him or her feeling happy and wanting to be a part of the group.

3. One thing I wish_____would do when I am around him or her is:_____

_____. If they do this I will feel better about including that person when I am around him or her.

4. Another thing I can try to change when I am around _____is_____

_____. This will keep him or her feeling happy and wanting to be a part of the group.

ONE THING THAT GETS ME REALLY *ANGRY* IS_____
_____. WHEN THIS HAPPENS, I'LL TRY TO BE CALM AND GIVE A MORE EXPECTED RESPONSE OR ONE THAT MATCHES THE SITUATION. This can really help keep the group together and everyone in the group wanting to continue to include me.

Getting Organized as a Group: Boss(y) versus Leader

Whenever you work or play as part of a group, one or two people usually take the lead to help the group get organized. If the group doesn't get organized around what they're to do together, the group falls apart.

Think of ways a group has to get organized even to play games together:

1.

2.

While a group works to get organized and stay together, each person has a job! Everyone in the group has to make an effort to stay in the group by keeping their eyes, bodies, and ears in the group. EACH person in the group has a job to try and figure out what the other people want to do. If a person in the group ONLY thinks about what he or she wants to do, this person is considered "selfish" or "bossy."

The difference between being a LEADER and being BOSSY:

People who take on being a LEADER make people want to work with them. Leaders often ask questions of the people they're leading or offer suggestions for everyone to consider. WHAT'S REALLY IMPORTANT IN GOOD LEADERS IS THAT THEY "LISTEN WITH THEIR EYES AND EARS" TO FIGURE OUT WHAT PEOPLE REALLY WANT TO DO. *For example*, a LEADER may see that someone in the group needs to move his body so that other people can play. If the leader says, "Why don't you move over here so David can see?," she is explaining why someone must do something.

If a leader tries to get some kids to decide what to do, what are some things the leader can say?

1.

2.

3.

4.

People who are BOSSY in a group often tell people what they should do, and they don't give them any choices. *Bossy* people make it seem like you must do it their way or they'll get mad at you. *For example*, if a bossy person wants someone to move her body somewhere else in the group, the bossy person will say "Move over here!"

Give some *examples* of what a BOSSY person would say to a group when the group members are trying to decide what to do.

1.

2.

3.

Giving and Receiving—Working in a Group on a Project

Working with others in a group can sometimes be tricky. Everyone has different ideas to add to the group, or someone may want to do a different task in the group. The hardest part is working together and deciding how this whole process will work. As social thinkers, we all try to add our thoughts or ideas while listening to ideas of others (receiving a suggestion).

The other tough part comes when someone doesn't agree with someone else. Sometimes we don't let people know we don't agree with them, and other times we do let them know. Deciding how to follow others' suggestions, even if we don't love their ideas, is a pretty fancy social skill. On the other hand, providing suggestions in a way people will want to use them also takes some skill. To do these things well, you have to consider the many ways in which people think about your plans (intentions) as you communicate with them. They pay attention to which words you use to talk to them, your tone of voice, your facial expression, etc.

Here are two *different examples* of people trying to give suggestions.

Do you think people will feel better about working with Mark or Jacob? They both are trying to give the same suggestion, but the way they go about it is different!

Mark makes a suggestion	Jacob makes a suggestion
"Hey, I know a better way to do this. You guys haven't thought of it and I know how to do this. We should write the paper by starting this way…" (As Mark says these things, he looks at the other members of his team with a serious tone of voice and an unfriendly look on his face.)	"I like your ideas; I have one too. Have you thought about writing the paper by starting this way?" (Jacob's tone of voice is friendly and he uses calm facial expressions while he says this.)

Answer: Jacob makes his suggestion in a way that doesn't put down the other members of the team. In fact, he states they had some good ideas. He also has a calm face and tone of voice. This makes people more willing to listen to his idea. They still might not accept his idea, but saying he likes their idea makes for a better discussion of everyone's ideas…so this is the better way.

Listed next are ideas for how to take suggestions and give suggestions in ways that make good or okay impressions on others. How do you let the person know your idea while still making a good impression?

Steps for Receiving a Suggestion

1. Stay calm.

2. Listen carefully to the suggestion.

3. Make no statements about why you think it may be a bad idea.

4. You don't have to say anything at all as a response to what others say as long as it looks like you are listening in a positive way (calm face, keeping your eyes thinking about the people who are talking).

5. If you make a different suggestion about how to approach the topic, do it in a way that doesn't make people feel bad about what they've already said.

6. Sometimes, if you're the only person who disagrees with what is suggested, you go along with the idea, even if you don't think it's perfect. This is called "cooperation." Cooperation means you give up demanding people should do things your way to allow other people in the group to make suggestions as well. (But the time when you don't cooperate is when you feel like the group is making decisions that put you in danger or are against the law!)

. . . .

Steps for Giving a Suggestion

1. Use a calm voice.

2. Have a calm or friendly facial expression.

3. Often, say something positive about others' ideas while they talk. That way, when you get ready to share your idea, it doesn't sound like you only will talk when it's about you telling people what they should think.

4. Any idea you suggest to the group is only a suggestion. Accept that they may not think it is as good an idea as you thought it was. To help you stay calm in this process, remember you did not think everyone else's idea was good either!

5. If you see yourself or others getting frustrated with this discussion-based process, try and remember that this is just a class project. It's better to figure out how to keep people wanting to work with you than to insist they use your ideas!

Group Plan versus My Plan

GROUP PLAN	MY PLAN
Brain: Thinking about the group activity or the other members of the group.	**Brain:** Thinking about whatever I want. Not thinking about what the group is thinking about.
Body: Doing what the group is doing and staying close to the group. If the group is jumping, I am jumping.	**Body:** Doing what I want, not what the group is doing. If the group is jumping and I am hopping, I'm following my plan, not the group's plan.
Eyes: Looking at others and looking at the group activity.	**Eyes:** Looking at what I want to look at (not what the group is looking at).
Words: Asking questions about the activity or about others, making suggestions, volunteering to help someone do something related to the activity, giving compliments, etc.	**Words:** Talking about what I want, not what the group is talking about. Talking about my own interests. Telling others what to do rather than making suggestions.

© 2011 Think Social Publishing, Inc. • www.socialthinking.com

Am I Following the Group's Plan or My Plan?

When you're in a group, you have to think about the other people in the group. What does each person want to do? What will be the group's plan? If you're only thinking of your own plan (like being silly), you're being a "just me" and not a "thinking of others" group member.

GROUP'S PLAN (adding to the fun)　　　　**MY PLAN** (taking away from the fun)

Group Project: Making a Commercial

Wow, you and your company got *rave reviews* for the awesome commercials that you put together for the Super Bowl. The reviews were so good that another company has asked for your help! A famous soda company, Popsi, wants to introduce a new soda product—and they want you to put together a catchy little commercial to air during the Super Bowl. The deadline is fast approaching. To make sure that you get it in on time, you'll work as a group to complete this task. Don't forget, you all need to help COME UP WITH THE SCRIPT, DIRECT, AND ACT IN THE COMMERCIAL.

To complete this task by the deadline, you all need to work together. What are some of the things that you need to consider when you work on a project as a group?

_____

_____

Do you need a leader? What might the leader do?

_____

_____

How do you get started? What is the plan?

_____

_____

Why are communication, participation, negotiation, and compromise important?

_____

_____

How do you use the *four steps of communication* to help you think about working with others in the group? How do you incorporate:

Thinking:

Body presence:

Eyes:

Words:

Bibliography

Beane, A. (2005). *The Bully Free Classroom: Over 100 Tips and Strategies for Teachers K-8.* Minneapolis, MN: Free Spirit Publishing. *www.freespirit.com*

Buron, K. and Curtis, M. (2003). *The Incredible 5-Point Scale. Assisting students with autism spectrum disorders in understanding social interactions and controlling their emotional responses.* Shawnee Mission, KS: Autism Asperger Publishing Company (AAPC). *www.asperger.net*

Cain, B. and Patterson, A. (2001). *Double-Dip Feelings: Stories to Help Children Understand Emotions.* Washington DC: Magination Press.

Crooke, P.J., Hendrix, R.E., and Rachman, J.Y. (2008). *"Brief Report: Measuring the Effectiveness of Teaching Social Thinking to Children with Asperger Syndrome (AS) and High Functioning Autism (HFA)."* Journal of Autism and Developmental Disorders, (38) 3.

Gajewski, N., Hirn, P., and Mayo, P. (1998). *Social Skill Strategies: A Social-Emotional Curriculum for Adolescence,* Book A (making impressions lessons: pages 116-121). WI: Thinking Publications. Now available in new edition at *www.superduperinc.com*

Myles, B., Trautman, M., and Schelvan, R. (2004). *The Hidden Curriculum: Practical Solutions for Understanding Unstated Rules in Social Situations.* Shawnee Mission, KS: Autism Asperger Publishing Company (AAPC). *www.asperger.net*

Packer, A. (1997). *How Rude! The Teenager's Guide to Good Manners, Proper Behavior, and Not Grossing People Out* (pages 152-179). Minneapolis, MN: Free Spirit Press.

Winner, M. (2000). *Inside Out: What Makes a Person with Social Cognitive Deficits Tick?* San Jose, CA: Think Social Publishing, Inc. *www.socialthinking.com*

Winner, M. (2007). *Social Behavior Mapping.* San Jose, CA: Think Social Publishing, Inc. *www.socialthinking.com*

Winner, M. (2005). *Think Social! A Social Thinking Curriculum for School-Age Students.* San Jose, CA: Think Social Publishing, Inc. *www.socialthinking.com*

Winner, M. (2007). *Thinking About YOU Thinking About ME,* 2nd edition. San Jose, CA: Think Social Publishing, Inc. *www.socialthinking.com*

Winner, M. and Crooke, P. (2009). *Socially Curious and Curiously Social.* San Jose, CA: Think Social Publishing, Inc. *www.socialthinking.com*

Crooke, P. and Winner, M. (2011). *Social Fortune or Social Fate?* San Jose, CA: Think Social Publishing, Inc. *www.socialthinking.com*

SocialThinking® has so much to offer!

OUR MISSION

At Social Thinking, our mission is to help people develop their social competencies to better connect with others and live happier, more meaningful lives. We create unique treatment frameworks and strategies to help individuals develop their social thinking and related social skills to meet their academic, personal and professional social goals. These goals often include sharing space effectively with others, learning to work as part of a team, and developing relationships of all kinds: with family, friends, classmates, co-workers, romantiç partners, etc.

ARTICLES

100+ free educational articles and treatment strategies

COURSES & TRAINING

15+ full-day courses and embedded training for schools and organizations

PRODUCTS

Books, games, posters, music and more!

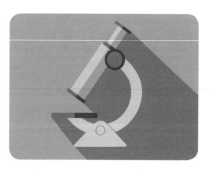

CLINICAL RESEARCH

Measuring the effectiveness of the Social Thinking Methodology

TREATMENT: CHILDREN & ADULTS

Clinical treatment, assessments, school consultations, etc.

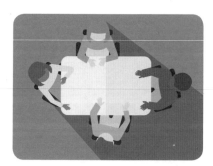

CLINICAL TRAINING PROGRAM

Three-day intensive training for professionals

www.socialthinking.com